The Captain
of
St. Margaret's

TWENTY FIVE
CHAPTERS OF MEMOIRS

The Captain
of
St. Margaret's

By FERENC MOLNAR

Translated by Barrows Mussey

NEW YORK
DUELL, SLOAN AND PEARCE

2

PRINTED IN THE UNITED STATES OF AMERICA
BY THE VAIL-BALLOU PRESS, INC., BINGHAMTON, N. Y.

The Captain
of
St. Margaret's

Prologue

ONE NIGHT IN PARIS I WAS STROLLING WITH GILBERT Miller, the New York producer, in front of the hotel where we were staying. We were discussing the architectural beauties of Paris.

Miller asked me: "From an artistic standpoint do you think that the Eiffel Tower is a beautiful structure?"

"I don't care to criticize the Eiffel Tower from any standpoint," I said, "because I cherish tender personal feelings toward it. My late father was once family physician to Eiffel, the architect, in Budapest."

Then I told him how Gustave Eiffel had erected several magnificent iron structures in my native Budapest, chief among them the St. Margaret Bridge. The St. Margaret Bridge, which spans the Danube at the southern point of St. Margaret's Island—I told Miller, whom I was trying to induce to go to Budapest—St. Margaret Bridge is a harmonious work of art in iron, bearing Eiffel's personality so strongly that the attentive passer-by seems to see the Eiffel Tower laid lengthwise across the broad river. And so I began to speak of St. Margaret's Island, the tiny, green, flower-bedecked isle that is our great pride. It was a little funny, but I was talking already like a tourist guide: I told my American friend that there are two hotels on the island, for the soil contains hot, medicinal, and sulphurous springs. I told him how, for twenty years, I had spent eight months of the year on the island, passing my youth there, so to speak, and if there was a spot on earth that I loved, that was it. I told him how beautiful the island is in spring, summer, and fall, and I mentioned that, above all, it had been loveliest one hard winter, white with great masses of snow, when the management kept the smaller hotel open, leasing it to a doctor who turned it into a sort of sanitarium for nervous diseases, and opened a winter season for hydropathic treatments.

Miller promised me that he would go to Budapest and live on this elfin island. We parted, and he returned to the hotel. For my part, I went on strolling up and down the Boulevard des Capucines for a long time because as a result of my tourist advertising the figure of a man from the past had risen unexpectedly in my memory, and with it the idea of writing a book about him.

When I say "from the past," I mean by past the period, including my own early youth, when not even a shadow of the war was cast on the future; a carefree, colorful, romantic world, since vanished, in a magic city, on the banks of the Danube. It was a world charming by night and not always charming by day. A world that took pains to be moral by day and immoral by night. A world that was more often beautiful than contemptible, and that was resurrected for a few years, to the notes of pure gypsy music, between the two world wars. Many of my American friends lived there at that time, and were fond of it. But this world even then was not as it had been, and it soon sank into oblivion. By "past" and "period" and "world" I mean a generation part of which has since died, and part of which —along with me—has grown old, suffering at home or wandering afar over the earth. A touch sentimental, that generation is now paying for the sins it was once so fond of.

I would like to begin the whimsical story of the man I mentioned above—into which I have shamefacedly smuggled a part of my own story as a sketchy biography—with the famous line that the Russian poet Pushkin set at the end of his immortal *Eugene Onegin*:

"Itak ya zhil togda v Odesse." This is how I lived in those days at Odessa.

Chapter I

DURING ONE WINTER A FEW YEARS BEFORE OUR FIRST
World War, I was among a group of fourteen living at the little hotel on St. Margaret's Island. Living there was interesting to a young journalist like
me, for the strange little group wintering in the
rather primitive three-story hotel consisted entirely
of odd characters—which hardly needs saying, for
normal people's nerves need no hydropathic treat-
ment. Malicious wags called our little hotel a miniature psychopathic asylum for the slightly crazy, but
we paid little heed to this slander.

For my part I needed no nerve cure at all. I had
always spent the winter in town, and this winter I
lived on the island solely because I had very little
money and because the Doctor, combining the func-
tion of lessee and chief physician, assured me it would
be very inexpensive—winking as he spoke, and looking at me as if he would not be annoyed in case I did
not pay even this modest price promptly. My view
of the matter later proved correct.

One day—it was an uncommonly cold, clear winter morning, a Sunday—I arrived exhausted after a
nocturnal conversation lasting until morning; I
came to the island in a sleigh since, owing to the deep

snow, all the cabmen had had to convert their hacks into sleighs. Near the little hotel (characterized in golden letters over the gate as a "Hydropathic Establishment") I got out of the sleigh. Just as I was paying off the cabman I saw to my utter amazement that a pillar of steam was rising, nay shooting, heavenward from the deep, virgin blanket of snow before the hotel. It was thickest at the bottom, grew more transparent as it went up, and finally evaporated at a remote height. This pillar of steam had not burst from the snow-covered ground, for it was moving. It moved ahead quite rapidly, going further and further from the hotel, and approaching a small building, visible in the distance, where the apothecary shop and the office of the management were quartered. My astonished eyes pursued it; then it turned off behind the little house, where it was visible for a few seconds above the low roof and then disappeared for good. Standing at the front door like a child, I felt I had witnessed a natural marvel.

The pillar of steam was not a natural marvel; the pillar of steam was an Imperial and Royal Captain of Cavalry. A living and breathing captain who was walking through the snow, steaming, that Sunday morning. He was giving off thick, real, white steam. He disappeared behind the little house because he was going to see the apothecary who lived there. Within a few minutes I learned all the details about my natural marvel—for it did not become a true marvel until it had all been explained to me.

Coming into the hotel, I found in the corner of the little lobby, near a large white-tiled stove, the remmants of a nocturnal card party that had evidently included drink. The gathering had already dispersed. The Doctor had chased out the "patients" when he found them arguing drunkenly by the stove at nine in the morning. The Doctor, poor fellow, was frantic because only the fourteen of us were living in the fifty rooms, and he could not raise anywhere the capital for this unprofitable enterprise. On the table stood the largest brandy bottle I have ever seen in my life. It was a big, bright green, fifteen-quart bottle, with a label marked *Szilvorium*, the popular name for plum brandy in Hungary. I heard that the monster bottle had been steered through the icebergs of the Danube in a steel skiff from old Buda, the suburb on the west bank of the Danube, from a cheap grog shop where these ungainly bottles stood in lieu of casks on the counter. There was very little of the brandy left at the bottom of the bottle. I also heard later that toward morning, when the cardplayers were already quite tight, they began to be hungry, and demanded soup. On the advice of the above-mentioned Captain they ate beer. They did not drink it, they ate it with spoons, from soup plates. According to the captain this was the best remedy for the evil results of drunkenness.

While I was gaping at the bottle and the plates, and trying to decide from the scattered cards what game the gentlemen had been playing, a faint tinkle came from the second floor. I knew that sound; it meant that the nurses were now tying the little bell to Baron Kalotay's wrist. The nurses always tied the bell to the Baron's hand before he went to bed. For the Baron—a lean, shaky, elderly man—was so feeble that if he woke up and wanted anything of the nurse, sleeping in the same room, he could neither call nor stretch out his paralyzed arm as far as the bell on the bedside table. He could just barely move enough to make the tiny bell ring if it were fastened to his wrist. And this man had played cards until morning along with the rest.

By now a bath attendant was at my side, describing the uproar in detail. The feeble Baron Kalotay, who was a rich man and a great cardplayer, had had himself carried in a red armchair, propped up on white pillows, down to the stove in the lobby the moment the Doctor had gone to bed. He had just now been carried upstairs. Smiling palely, he sat on his white pillows in the red armchair, which two bath attendants were transporting to the upper floor; he took mutely the scolding of the Doctor, who was walking along beside the chair, abusing him. He was being put to bed now; hence the tinkling.

Then I saw the Mayor sitting on the red-carpeted

stairs for a few minutes longer. His Honor the former mayor of a small town in northern Hungary was the only real madman in the party. He too had played cards until morning.

He sat on the stairs until the energetic voice of the Doctor could be heard behind him also. Then he jumped up with a start and ran for his room, laughing loudly. Although I barely touch upon him in this story, I must point out one thing about the Mayor: he was a novelist. For months he had been working on a great society novel, which I am sure was interesting, but which no one could read, because His Honor had a very impractical method of writing. He was setting down the whole novel on a single sheet of paper. When he started, he covered a page from top to bottom. Then instead of taking a new sheet he continued again at the top of the same page. When he showed me the novel he had already been working on it for six months. Considering that he used to write six or eight hours a day, always on the same sheet, it must have been a very long novel. There was not a trace of writing left on the paper. It might have been dyed black with ink—it had simply turned into black paper. The Mayor, however, wrote merrily on, day after day. This novel manuscript of the Mayor's is no invention of mine; it is a fact, known to the history of psychopathology. Whenever I told the story at a party I used to be in the habit of adding facetious remarks, such as,

"This method is to be recommended to a great many authors." I have since discovered that the mere fact is more effective without such remarks. There is no harm in my telling it here, for it is an organic part of the picture from which clouds of steam rose heavenward.

Chapter II

THE PILLAR OF STEAM—THE CAPTAIN—HAD DRUNK a terrific quantity of the homemade plum brandy, lost all his money, and run up debts with the feeble Baron Kalotay and a blond Transylvanian count with a delicate face who had been the first to leave the card table when the Doctor detected and scattered the party. The Doctor was growling at the Captain, too, in the way doctors do at disobedient patients. The Captain gave him fiery glances, tolerated his scolding, and meanwhile began to dress. He put on his heavily lined, long, brown military greatcoat, pulled the hilt of his sword through the slitted left pocket that was customary before the war, put on his cap, and made as if to leave the Doctor standing there. The latter, however, barred his way, insisting that he must at once take a tepid bath with an ice-cold compress on his head. Under no circumstances could he go to bed in this condition without a bath.

The Captain did not want to take a bath. The

Doctor laughed, and tried to use force. He had the gate locked. The Captain laughed too, but refused to take a bath. Finally, with great difficulty, the Doctor and attendants pushed him into the hall of the water-cure establishment, where the big wooden tubs stood. The Captain reared up, ejaculated some incomprehensible order or other, snatched his sword from its sheath, got into a wooden tub just as he was, in uniform, boots, and greatcoat, and turned on the warm water. Not a soul could get near him now (the chief attendant told me afterward), for he brandished his heavy cavalry saber, and threatened to split the skull of anyone who approached. The tub filled up with hot water.

When it was full to the brim, the Captain sat down to his neck in the water. Only his head with the cap and his drawn sword rose above the water level. He laughed delightedly, and asked the Doctor (rushing desperately to and fro, looking for help) whether he was satisfied now. Then, after soaking in the hot water for ten minutes or so, he got out of the tub, keeping everyone at a distance with his terrible swift sword, and went out of the door, just as he was, into the snow. He was going to the apothecary's to take some cognac. All he said as he went out was that if the apothecary had still failed to get cognac glasses, and they had to drink the cognac out of test tubes again, he would cut the man down. As he stepped out of the door into the biting winter cold, still dripping, and weighed down by the pounds of hot water that his thickly lined greatcoat had soaked up like a sponge, he suddenly turned into a pillar of steam. I am told he was at his best as he went out of the door; at that moment the steam rose from him to the sky. I did not see him until his vapor had come down to the height of a house.

When I started up the stairs to bed at last, I heard the Doctor's voice behind me. "Just got home?"

"Just this minute."

"At nine in the morning?"

"Just about."

"Where did you sleep?"

"Nowhere. I'm going to sleep now."

He gave a low, hoarse laugh. "A terrible patient."

"I'm no patient of yours," I said. "When you rented me this room, I expressly told you I was not a patient here, but only a hotel guest."

"All right, all right," he said soothingly, "don't get excited. I'd say I've come a long way—I'm talking to someone who's proud of not being my patient. But . . . if you won't mind my asking you a question. Aren't you in the habit of sleeping at all?"

"Now and then."

"When?"

"By day."

"And do you get enough sleep?"

"Never."

"And what do you do at night?"

"I write. With pen, on paper. Also, I live my private life then. It's quiet at night, and you can get your work done in the back rooms of all-night cafés. The society I move in, gentlemen and ladies both, mostly sleeps by day too."

"Fine sort of society, I must say."

"It isn't exactly the elite of Budapest society, but I like it. If I ever get to be a successful elderly author, I shall sleep at night and move in better society."

He looked at me with a mixture of envy and contempt. "You're quite a strange young man."

"I hope I am," I said, feeling rather flattered, as I went upstairs.

It was all the fault of a little black-haired girl, a student at a second-rate theatrical school, with whom the Captain was madly in love. She called herself Mercedes Pallay, apparently a stage name. He had really become utterly infatuated with this gypsy-eyed, otherwise rather insignificant little girl, who apparently did not much care about him. On the evening before this wild night he had arranged a rendezvous with her. They were to take supper together. The Captain went to fetch her where she lived, in a furnished room, but she was not at home.

The landlady opened the door, and delivered her message: "Miss Mercedes is very sorry, but she isn't going to supper with the Captain, because she had an invitation from Mr. Oskar." Oskar was a limping vaudeville agent, from whom the young lady had hopes of a career. The Captain thrust the landlady aside, and rushed into the room, for he did not believe any of this. But the room was empty.

Thereupon, deeply embittered, he went alone to the Hotel Hungaria, where he got drunk on champagne. Then he hired a sleigh, and went home through the night to St. Margaret's Island. That is, he had himself driven only as far as the bridge. At the bridgehead he ordered the cabman to take his seat in the sleigh. He mounted the driver's seat, and charged down the causeway and along the two miles of the main street on the island to the hotel, in a way that you used to see in the old silent films, with terrified Russians fleeing in sleighs from the madly galloping pack of hungry wolves in Siberia. That was the beginning of this memorable night.

The Captain was a thickset, very powerful man. The characteristic point about his face was a jutting jawbone. He had thick, stiff, reddish hair, as refractory as horsehair, but he tormented it with wet brushes until it stuck together somehow. He wore a little rust-colored mustache. His eyes were dark, halfway between blue and violet. Usually he looked piercingly at anyone who was speaking to him. He would laugh loud and heartily at even the most simple-minded jest; then his bony peasant face would become somehow endearing, and you saw why he always forced himself to look piercing: if he did not, he would always have the look of a five-year-old child listening to a fairy tale. He was a passionate and prolific storyteller. Whenever an argument arose in this company over any subject, you could be sure of his throwing light on the question with some story, usually drawn from his own life.

And his name? In the course of this account I shall have things to tell of him that make it seem advisable to withhold his name.

Chapter III

THAT NIGHT I CAME HOME TO THE ISLAND ABOUT half past two from the office of the *Budapesti Naplo* newspaper. I found only a small group still seated around the table in the little restaurant at the hotel. The Doctor, the Mayor, Baron Kalotay, and the Captain were sitting around a bottle. It must have contained some very strong drink, for they were drinking from tiny glasses—though very frequently, it must be admitted. I joined them. The row of sparkling streetlights on the east bank glimmered across the Danube through the big windows in the clear winter night. I don't know what they had been talking about, but when I joined them, the Captain was saying:

"I owe my life to a murder."

Not a trace of the previous night was left about

him. He was not shrouded in a cloud of steam now, but wore the gold-laced blue uniform of a Hungarian Hussar officer with the three stars of a captain's rank on his collar.

"It was like this," the Captain went on. "I was madly in love with a girl who had married someone else. I was twenty years old, and I thought it was the end of the world. I decided to commit suicide. Please don't smile. If ever there was a typical candidate for suicide, I'm it. To this very day. It's a family trait. In a word, at nine o'clock one evening I went into the town woods, among the tall bushes, carrying in my pocket a brief farewell note to the faithless girl, and a beautiful dark blue revolver to shoot myself with. That evening was not the first time I had been there. I had been wandering around there every night for four nights. I reflected deeply; indeed I confess I sometimes wept. I touched and studied the revolver. I unbuttoned the shirt over my chest, and then buttoned it up again. Twice I fell asleep in the woods, and didn't come wandering home until daybreak. I thought about putting it off, but I was resolved to end my life. The anguish over the girl was unbearable. Life without her seemed meaningless.

"Well, the night of that fourth day I made up my mind. Behind a big bush I took out the revolver and pointed it at my heart. I shut my eyes tight, tensely, the way you do at the dentist's when you feel the cold steel in your tooth. I clenched my teeth, and squeezed the trigger. But in the hundredth of a second between my decision and the execution, the revolver jerked in my hand. It's a movement that a man wants to make, and at the same time he doesn't want to. It happens even with practiced suicides. At the last moment, from somewhere, no one knows where, perhaps from the bottom of your subconscious, comes a twitch, a tremendously quick, sure little movement, pointing the weapon at life instead of death. It's a sacred, ultimate reflex that only those who have once gone this far know about. Apparently it takes long practice for a man's hand to be steady against himself. In a word, the revolver was not looking my heart in the eye when it spat out the bullet, but beyond my heart. There was a slight graze on my skin, a slight blow, but the bullet did not go into my body; it went off somewhere into the bushes.

"At the same instant I heard the quick outcry, a man's anguished voice. 'Oh!' And then I heard the thud of a human body. Revolver in hand, I came out of the bushes. The man lay speechless on the ground. I knelt down beside him, and felt for his wrist. He had no pulse. I laid my head to his heart. Not a sound. 'Good God,' I said, horrified; 'why, the man's dead.' I peered around, listening. In the nocturnal stillness of the woods, not a sound, not a soul. I felt in the dead man's pockets. I wanted to know who he was; why I didn't run off, I can't tell you. Possibly because I now knew for sure that I would really have to shoot myself within a few minutes. As I say, I felt in his pockets. There I found a letter, not sealed. On the envelope was a woman's address. Let's say, 'Mathilde Kelen, Andrassy ut 155.' The substance of the letter was roughly as follows. Salutation, 'My adored angel, my all.' Then the poor devil wrote that he was writing this letter late at night, after long pondering. He wrote: 'Today I have definitely made up my mind. I consent; belong to another, marry, become the wife of K. R., and live happily. I shall never forget the heavenly moments I spent in your arms. I know that circumstances compel you to give up me, the pauper boy, to marry a well-to-do older man whom you don't love.' Here the pauper boy spoke rather disdainfully about the well-to-do elderly gentleman by the name of K. R. Then the letter went on: 'As late as yesterday I was sure I would kill myself because I could not endure the agonizing pain of longing for you. I even bought the revolver whose purpose was to be the erasing of my tortured existence. But I have come to a different conclusion. I have thrown away the revolver. My adored angel, I will live for you, I will fight and win to be worthy of your love.' "

The Captain paused briefly. He smiled. "All hollow phrases, utterly commonplace; it sounds very comical today, I know, but then, read there in the bushes by the faint light of a match, it was touching, it was even beautiful. The letter went on: 'My brother, who loves and pities me very much, is willing to give me money enough to go to America, to work and make money. I am young, my beloved, my all; all is not yet lost. Living with K. R. you cannot forget me; I feel it, I know it. Beyond doubt I shall come back a rich man. You will divorce K. R. and belong to me. My bosom now is full of hope and ambition. Write me a line, if only the address on an empty envelope, so that I can recognize your writing. It will give me even more strength for the battle I shall fight so that some day you can belong to me.' That was about how the letter read. At the end were several 'I worship you's' and 'My life's' and 'Devotedly yours unto death's,' and so forth.

"Stirred to the depths, I surveyed the dead man as he lay there with his face in the dust of the road, turned sidewise, his coat bloodstained, his eyes half open. His face still wore the expression of astonishment, indeed of horror, with which he must have called out 'Oh!' just before.

"What took place now, gentlemen, was a decisive event in my life. I reached into my coat pocket. 'I wrote a farewell note too,' I said to the dead man. As I have mentioned, my note was short. What it said was: 'My dearest beloved: God speed you. I shall shoot myself tonight in the town woods. When you read these lines, I shall no longer be among the living. My last thought is of you.' 'Darling boy' was the signature. (My faithless one had chosen to call me so.) I took the letter out of the envelope, put it in the envelope addressed to Mathilde Kelen, sealed it, and stowed it in the dead man's pocket. 'This too I will give you,' I whispered to him, putting my revolver in the dust beside him. Then I stooped down tenderly to him and kissed his forehead. 'I'm going to America,' I said to him softly. 'Goodbye.'

"I took the letter addressed to Mathilde. I got up, brushed the dust off my knees, buttoned up my shirt over my chest, looked for my hat in the bushes, and continued the stroll that the other had so suddenly and unexpectedly interrupted. I could feel my feet carrying me more buoyantly, my lungs working more hotly, my heart pounding harder. My heart began to sing with drunken exultation. I walked fast. 'I'm going to America,' I said so loud that my own voice scared me. I seemed already to see the ship, spewing thick black smoke from her stacks, the blue sea. Many little colored flags flew from the ship. Although I did not realize it, a poster from a steamer line was dominating my imagination. Blue sky, black smoke, white ship, hundreds of little red, yellow, green, orange pennants, fastened to a rope, flapping in the wind. I could smell the fresh, keen sea wind. I saw ports with millions of grimy, hardworking laborers. I saw myself in the future: reading the paper at home on Sunday afternoon in slippers and shirtsleeves after a hard week's work, beside me the faithless one, now my wife, embracing me with a sweet smile, and at my feet played a child, our child. And again and again the sea, the sea! America! My heart, my brain, my whole life seemed to sing so joyfully that I had to lean against a tree with my eyes closed, half swooning."

The Captain introduced another pause. One could see how the memory stirred him. Then he simply said: "I stayed three years in America. I didn't get rich. I started off as a riding-master in New York, in Central Park. I came back to Europe as a stowaway. I never saw the faithless girl again. But I had my life; and I still have it."

Then the Captain asked for his check. "I had eleven plum brandies," he said to the waiter, paid, and went to his room.

Before we went to sleep we took a little stroll in the snow along the bank of the Danube in the cold moonlight. Silence lay over the island. The thin willow twigs hung motionless in the calm. We realized we had been listening to a monstrous fabrication— one so great that even Nature herself seemed speechless in the face of it.

The others discussed the question of whether the Captain's story might possibly have been true after all. Leaving them, I went to my room and lay down. I decided it made no difference to me whether the story had been true or not. In my eyes storytelling wherein the narrator himself plays a part gives a great insight into the storyteller's character. Probably this is because the narrators have no idea that by the very manner of the tale they are characterizing themselves. This is particularly true if they are lying.

Chapter IV

THE CAPTAIN'S MOST INTIMATE FRIEND ON THE IS-land was the "apothecary," Mr. Feher. Young Mr. Feher, a tall, bony, blond lad, was not the proprietor of the apothecary shop, but only a student of pharmacy who managed the tiny store, and whose pharmacological knowledge sufficed—if he had not had too much to drink—to keep him from confusing linseed oil with licorice juice. His name was Feher, Ladislas Feher, but I never heard anyone call him Feher or Ladislas. Everyone called him Pharmaco, and he explained proudly to all the chambermaids in the hotel that this name came from an ancient Greek word, *pharmakon*, which meant medicine, and also poison.

His intimate friendship with the Captain requires explanation on two counts. Firstly, how they became acquainted, and secondly, how they grew fond of each other.

Firstly. In the summer there were always a great many songbirds on the island, but only one nightingale, the apothecary. Pharmaco was young, and a poet on the side. He wrote Hungarian folksongs and

set them to music. His instrument was the tradi-
tional instrument of young people working in lab-
oratories: the ancient wind instrument formed of
upper and lower lips. He was lean and restless, and
wanted to be conspicuous at any price, for he came
from a small village where he had really counted,
and now he was depressed by a feeling that he was
lost in the big city. So, when the summer night was
fine and the patrons of the waters were strolling in
groups around the hotels, he would hide at midnight,
in a tall patch of shrubbery, and here by the hour
he would imitate the nightingale. He did it exceed-
ingly well, so well that even I would sometimes sit
down on a nearby bench and listen dreamily although I knew it was he—indeed even though I
could sometimes see the thin smoke of his cigarette
rising silvery in the moonlight from the shrubbery.
The Captain, who was passionately fond of night-
ingales, once happened to hear it, and upon discover-
ing that the apothecary was the nightingale, he
rushed into the bushes and introduced himself. From
then on they would often sit hidden in the shrubbery; Pharmaco would whistle, and the Captain
would listen. The nightingale songs on the island
came to an end because the Captain began bringing
Hennessy Three Star brandy into the shrubbery to
the songbird. Too bad. The Captain poisoned the
nightingale, and the nightingale's song was heard no
more. Later, however, the tuneful music of the bird

was often replaced at night by jolly folksongs with quite shameless words, which could be heard sounding from the bushes, so that the promenading young ladies would flee, horrified.

That was only their first acquaintance. Their affection, however, began over the horsecar. The little horse-drawn tram, the darling of us all, was a one-horse car plying between the southern and northern tips of the island, down a double avenue of century-old trees, so that even in the hot summer it went through a high-vaulted, green, shadowy, cool tunnel. The horsecar was pulled by the horses of pensioned generals. Retired elderly soldiers, mostly friends of old Archduke Joseph, would put out their favorite horses, which they no longer liked to mount —owing to the superannuation partly of the horse, partly of the rider—to board here. They were cared for until they died, fed by the faithful, quiet peasant coachmen of the Archduke. To this day I don't know why they needed horses for that horse tram, for the light, open car rolled of itself. I never saw the traces tight except at the moment of starting off. Even at that a slight push would have started the car; then it ran quietly along the tracks, the rope dangling wearily like a clothesline in the wind, while the well-fed pony trotted in the lead with head inclined sideways—mostly, no doubt, to show the car the way. On Sundays the old generals came out to call on their horses, bringing lump sugar. This was the horsecar line whose monotonous to-and-fro was interrupted by the Captain and the apothecary—only once, and that was the night when they became fast friends.

The Captain had invited a group of ladies to dinner at the southern end of the island. After dinner there was dancing, and just as the dance was in full swing, exactly at midnight, the landlord closed the place and sent away the gypsy band. Curfew.

The apothecary rushed to the stables, and bribed two horsecar drivers. Half an hour later anyone who was out for a nocturnal promenade on the dark main street of the island might have seen the following through the shrubbery: open horsecars moving at a quiet trot one close behind the other, between the rows of trees. The light of oil lanterns lit up both. There were great doings in the leading one, for the Captain was dancing the czardas with his guests. The rhythmic intensity of the Hungarian czardas is extremely great, but the area required is very small. In the second car sat the gypsy orchestra, making music. Pharmaco was the liaison officer between the two cars; he would dance for a while in the first car, go back to the second to encourage the gypsies, give the driver a cigar, and regulate the interval between the two cars.

So the two trams drove up and down the two-mile stretch, making music, until six in the morning. For that, telling the story again after many years, we can love Pharmaco. No wonder the Captain, whose party he had thus rescued, and indeed made famous, became devoted to him from that day forward. For a long time I never heard him make but one critical observation upon the apothecary, when he happened to say: "I tell you, Pharmaco is an angel, but you couldn't exactly call him a strictly cleanly angel. I happened to see him in the morning when he was washing. His room is hard to heat, and cold as ice. He's too lazy to heat water. So he just washes his hands with a little cold water. He simply powders his neck heavily with a powder puff. He says he learned it from a Norwegian actor who was the best Romeo in the northernmost city of the continent, at Hammerfest."

Only once were the Captain and Pharmaco adversaries. They made a bet, and appointed me referee. It was as to which of the two could eat the more revolting things. It was all my fault, for at supper I had said I was surprised at the Captain's eating snails. As referee I gave the signal to start. Pharmaco went out to the restaurant kitchen, came back with, and ate, a small fish alive. This won great applause. Thereupon the Captain bit off a piece of a thin wineglass, chewed it to a powder, and swallowed it. Pharmaco now consumed the front page of a newspaper, all fair and square down to the last line. Thereupon the Captain ate three splendid Maréchal Niel roses. It would not have been so bad in itself, but he next dined upon one of those flowers bearing the name of Georgina, which are no doubt colorful and beautiful to look at, but have a smell that has always made me shudder. In my opinion the Captain had won the bet with the flowers. If I had not given him the verdict, dreadful things would have ensued, for the Captain said he would now eat a dish called "fried queens." He went into the kitchen with a pack of playing cards, and ordered the four queens fried, just like chicken, in hot butter with bread crumbs. At the same time I saw Pharmaco come running with a handful of May beetles.

Chapter V

I WAS FIFTEEN YEARS YOUNGER THAN THE CAPTAIN. He treated me like a child, but not, I must say, without kindness. He seemed to feel a faint surprise at my mysterious craft; he thought it very funny that I would sit down in front of a piece of paper and simply write it full of stories out of my head. Sometimes, in an access of vanity, I am inclined to think the Captain even admired me a little for this.

Once he came into my room and said, "Sit down and write before my eyes. I want to see how you do it."

I sat down and did as he asked. He smoked and looked at me in silence for fifteen minutes. Now and then he would look at my scribblings, to make sure I was really writing down sentences. Having convinced himself that it was not a fraud, he shook his head. Then he asked for the sheet of paper, and read what I had written.

"Tremendous," he said.

The praise was intended not for what he had read, but for the fact that I could simply write a piece of paper full of stuff just out of my head.

"What paper do you write for?" he asked.

"The *Budapesti Naplo*."

"The other day you listened very carefully to the story I was telling."

"It was interesting," I said.

"A good many things have happened to me during my life," he returned with a bitter smile. "It would be worth while writing my biography. A clever boy like you could write it."

"Not a bad idea," I said.

"I suppose a life story like that," he inquired, "would have to begin with my birth?"

"They usually do."

"Shall I tell you how I was born?"

"Please do."

He laughed aloud. "I was born," he said, "like Napoleon. Not in my mother's bed, but in our dining room. Did you know how Napoleon was born? One Sunday morning his mother was coming back from Mass. On the way to the bedroom she felt the

birth pangs in the dining room. She didn't have time
to get to the bedroom. She brought Napoleon into
the world in the dining room. That's the only common point in our life stories. As a soldier I was a little
behind him." He laughed at his own joke. My silence
was polite, but rather painful.

"My premature birth, so to speak, was of more
interesting origin. To tell the truth, a dreadful origin."

To be honest, I had suspected that the very story
of the Captain's birth was bound to be an unusual
one, particularly if he were to tell about it himself.

He continued. "It must have been terrible. My
mother was pregnant, but she did not expect me for
three weeks. One evening after supper she went out
for a walk with my father in the park of the Medical School across the way. They came home after ten
o'clock. The front door of the building was a little
open, although according to regulations it should
have been locked at ten o'clock. They came into
the archway. A ghastly spectacle met their eyes. In
the dim light of the archway lay a severed human
head, the head of an old man with a frightful slash
in his face. Beside the head lay a woman with bleeding forehead. And beside the woman knelt a young
man with a knife in his hand, about to cut open the
woman's stomach. My mother gave a scream. My
father leaped upon the murderer and wrested the
knife from his hand. My mother swooned. Father

carried her to our apartment. As he was dragging her through the dining room, I suddenly came into the world before he got my mother into the bedroom, on the dining-room carpet. Just like Napoleon."

He paused for effect. I too said nothing, waiting for the explanation.

"The explanation," he said, "is fundamentally very simple. A young doctor lived in a plain furnished room in the building. He was working in the anatomical section of the Medical School, and very busily too, because he was just about to be appointed assistant professor. He used to work in the anatomical section until late at night. When the section was closed in the evening, and the young doctor had to leave, he often wrapped up parts of human cadavers in paper, and brought them home to go on working with them at night. No one in the building knew about this. The janitor merely saw that he used to come home with packages. On that memorable night he brought home a human head wrapped in paper. The outside door was already locked. As you know, the subtenants have no key; at night they have to ring for the janitor to open the door for them. The young doctor rang, and the janitor's wife opened the door. The doctor, coming into the archway, suddenly remembered that he had no cigarettes. He said to the janitor's wife, 'Do you mind waiting a minute? I'll just run over to the café and get some cigarettes.' So saying, he put his package on the floor against the wall, and dashed out.

"The janitor's wife was an inquisitive woman. Unable to resist the temptation, she opened the package, and the human head rolled out of the paper at her feet. She was so terrified that she fainted and crashed to the floor, and injured her head.

"The doctor came back with his cigarettes, and of course his first thought was to bring the unconscious woman around. He knelt down beside her, and began by trying to loosen the woman's tight corset. Unskilled in the mysteries of corsets, he could not get this one undone. So he quickly took out his knife to cut it open. At that moment my mother and father came into the archway. That is why I was born on August third instead of August twenty-fourth. I gained three weeks from Fate, if the time one spends alive can be called a gain. This might make the first chapter of my biography."

I did not consider it necessary to make any critical annotation to this "first chapter." It was strange, but not impossible. After a brief silence the Captain reverted to Napoleon. He pronounced his name reverently.

"Napoleon! . . ." he said. "Did you ever read Las Cases' book about Napoleon? Marquis Las Cases went into exile with him on the island of St. Helena, and wrote down everything the Emperor said there. That's pretty much how I imagine the book you're going to write about me. We're living on an island too, and more or less in exile, aren't we?"

I grinned in embarrassment, and he went on, "As a soldier I admire only the soldier in Napoleon. Do you know when I think he was most a soldier? On the island of St. Helena, when, as Las Cases tells us, he once read the Bible aloud to his companions after supper. There was always reading after supper in the drawing-room of his little house. Usually he did the reading himself. One evening he read aloud from the Old Testament—the Book of Judith. As he read, recalling his campaign in the East, he would pause over the name of each village mentioned in the Bible, and say, 'I pitched camp there.' 'I took that with a cavalry charge.' 'That was where my artillery was posted.' 'From that point I watched the battle through a spyglass,' and so on. Isn't it touching?"

I said, "Las Cases is not reliable. According to the Encyclopedia Britannica, his memoirs should be read with great caution. And the Book of Judith is an apocryphal part of the Old Testament."

He looked at me like a child close to tears. "All that proves is," he said, "that you're not a soldier, but a bookworm."

Chapter VI

ONE MORNING WHEN I WAS COMPELLED TO STAY AT the hotel because so much snow had fallen during the night that you could not get a sleigh out from town by telephone to drive you in for all the money in the world, I had just finished stoking my little iron stove when the Captain came home.

"Do you write stories for the newspaper?"

"I do some of that, too."

"Well, then I'll tell you the story of my hussar greatcoat. If you like you can write it out. But see that you don't mention my name, or I'll cut you down."

"We aren't in the habit of doing that," I said modestly.

"Well, listen to this." And he told the story.

"One evening when I was a young officer I had an inspection in barracks. I was lying fully dressed on my iron cot, waiting for the time to pass.

"Suddenly the telephone rang. Local army headquarters was on the wire. I was to take a detachment of hussars at once to the house at No. 98 Jozsef Utca. The house was on fire, and the fire department was working, but the crowd of curiosity-seekers in the street was so large that the police had requested military support. It was a common occurrence.

"We were there within ten minutes. Smoke, a red glare in the sky, rivers of water in the street. Not a word had to be said to the crowd. They divided of their own accord when they heard the quick trot of the cavalry horses from afar—like the Red Sea before the Jews. The poor firemen were working, clambering, splashing, whistling, and running. They deluged everyone with water, and in another ten minutes they were dripping as if not fire but water had broken out in the house. But all in vain, a three-story house had burned down, and the fire had conscientiously destroyed it, burning it to the cellar.

"The best part of it was that when I started to light a cigarette, the police captain courteously pointed out that no smoking was allowed. See here, you ought to write that as a separate story some time, with the title 'Nonsense!'

"In short, I looked on and waited until it was over. The investigating group went into the smoking ruins: police officers, fire department inspectors in white asbestos coats, with huge brass helmets. I told them I would go along with them. There was a great to-do in the street outside; the police were not letting anyone into the building, although a few were wailing that they lived there, and had run home at the news that they had burned down. Well, we went into the smoking darkness with this investigating group; two firemen clambered up the ruined stairs ahead of us, lighting our way with uplifted torches. On the third floor, where the back hall had not quite collapsed, we went through thick smoke into an apartment. There were remnants of furniture, in which the treacherous fire was still crawling slyly about as if trying to escape. On the floor by the wall we saw a blackened heap of something. A fireman held his torch in that direction. A woman and a man. Charred. But closely embracing. An awful embrace in the face of death, at the moment of death, beyond death. The doorman's wife, standing behind me, screamed so loud that we all froze. Who was it? 'Mrs. X,' she said. 'Mr. and Mrs. X lived in this apartment.' I inquired: 'Is that her husband?' 'Oh, no,' she said, 'her husband is in front, wrangling with the police because they won't let him in until everything has been investigated. He was not at home when the fire started.' I inquired: 'Who is the unfortunate man she was hugging?' 'I don't know,' said the doorman's wife. I risked another question: 'Was she good looking?' She said, 'Very pretty.'

"I was very much touched. 'Well, Hussar,' I said to myself, 'this is your chance to show that you're a gentleman.' Don't be horrified, my boy, put yourself in my place. At that awful moment a woman's honor was in my hands. A dead woman's honor. Already the chief investigator, an inspector in a white smock, was saying, 'Come, gentlemen, let's get going.' What to do? I couldn't go on until this was taken care of. What a situation! Was I to take a beam and make the entwined pair unrecognizable? I would never have a quiet moment until the end of my days if I had done that to two human bodies, even though they were charred. Sweat poured down my forehead from under my shako. I took off my overcoat and spread it over the lovers. Then I dragged across a beam, half of which was still glowing, and put it on the coat, and then everything else half-burned that I could find—a chair, a closet door. My hands were covered with burns. The investigating group was long since elsewhere, while I still struggled to set my coat on fire, so as to burn the lovers, the beam, and the little pyre into a shapeless mass. In vain I asked a fireman to help me light the coat with his torch; he said he was there to put out fires, not to start them. You can write about that, too, in a special chapter. The title might be, 'Nonsense, Continued.'

"Finally the coat did catch, and with it the funeral pyre I had built. I stood over it until everything around the lovers was on fire, inextricably fused with them. It was awful, but the new fire set the two to blazing again. When I left, it was all one formless black mass. The husband was no doubt still among those arguing with the police downstairs, trying to get in. What happened afterward I don't know. I had done my duty."

Having told this, he stared for some time without saying anything. Then suddenly he jerked his head up. "Whoa," he said, "there's something wrong about this."

I looked at him inquiringly.

"If you write it as a short story," he said, "the husband will find out now what happened then. There aren't so many husbands in the world whose wives have got burned up while they were away. He'll recognize the circumstances."

"Well, then I won't write it. Maybe I will after many years, when I get old."

"Well, for that matter," he said after a moment's reflection, "if you were to move the whole story into the provinces or abroad . . . And anyway, it's pretty nearly twenty years ago now."

The possibility flashed through my suspicious young newspaper head that the story might not be true. I wrote it, and it was printed, slightly changed, in the *Budapesti Naplo*. The day the story appeared, he came toward me with the paper in his hand. He slapped it savagely.

"Isn't it good?" I asked, dismayed.

"I can't tell about that," he replied. "Probably not, if it was written by you. But one thing I object to strongly, that you called me not a cavalryman but an infantryman. I wouldn't have expected that of you. I gather from that that privately you think I'm a very low sort of soldier."

I referred to the fact that he had wanted me to

change the story around because the husband might still be living somewhere today, after twenty years. Then I said: "Anyway, I never in my life heard of cavalry's being ordered to fires. I've often been to fires as a reporter, and I still remember the stereo-typed sentence: 'A battalion of the Thirty-second Infantry Regiment arrived on the double under the command of Captain X. Y.' " My heart was almost pounding as I waited for his answer.

He was rather confused. "Nowadays that may possibly be so. In my time hussars used to restore order on such occasions. It wasn't kind of you to do that to my feelings. You have hurt me."

For a few days he was quite chilly. He greeted me amiably, and we chatted, but he would not, for in-stance, creep up behind me as he had used to do when I was out for a walk alone in the snow, to give me a slap on the back.

I could not get it out of my head that he had said, "You have hurt me." This injured my feelings. I had written the story, not really on account of the story itself, but chiefly to give him pleasure. That is, I wanted to be kind to him. I had hurt him. Unin-tentionally. I would brood over how I was ap-parently not a kind person, for such accidents did not usually happen to really kind people. I con-soled myself with the reflection that it was not enough to be kind, but you also had to have luck. And afterward I saw an incident confirming this theory of mine. It happened in the fall of 1914, during the first months of the World War. War wounded were arriving in Budapest for the first time, on a long railroad train. A great crowd was standing around the station, gaping at the grisly spectacle to which in the course of years they became so accustomed—bleeding men, handled by the hundreds like railway freight. This particular load was all Russian prisoners of war. When we newspapermen arrived, their stretchers were already unloaded side by side in the square before the station. The poor fellows were moaning loudly. The doctors went to them in turn by torchlight, and we followed the doctors. K, a reporter, was the one most upset. A really kind and tenderhearted man, he turned pale at the sight, and looked upon this blood-stained misery, still new at the time, with deep pity. He stopped beside a gigantic black-bearded Russian, who was wailing the loudest of any. Next to him stood the Hungarian doctor, who spoke some sort of broken Russian, and was able to make the soldier understand him.

My friend K inquired, "What's this fellow bellowing about?"

"He says," said the doctor, "that at the front there was a rumor going around that the Hungarians execute all prisoners of war. Now he's bawling because he's afraid of that."

My friend K was honestly indignant. "Unheard

of!" he cried. "Shameful lying propaganda! We must reassure this poor man at once. Let's show him our love and sympathy."

So saying, he stepped over to the Russian, smiled tenderly at him, and began to pat him kindly on the shoulder. The Russian replied to this amiability with a frightful roar. That shoulder was where the bullet had lodged.

As I say, it is not enough to be kind; you need luck as well.

Chapter VII

GRADUALLY THE CAPTAIN FORGOT HOW I HAD offended him. When I felt that he had forgiven me, I told him my above-mentioned theory of kindness. I pointed out to him how infinitely few really kind and good people there were in the world. Even Jesus had not considered himself good. When someone came and called him "Good Master," He said: "Why callest thou me good? None is good save one, that is, God."

The Captain said, "There aren't many good, kind people, but still there are more than there are bad ones. Wait till you're a few years older, and you'll find out. A really bad man is the greatest of rarities."

"What do you consider a really bad man?"

"One who has no excuse for a bad action."

"Who has any excuse?"

"Well, for example, a cripple. Or a nervously irritable person. Or a very poor, starving man. Or someone who knows he has cancer. Or a person that has been cheated by a great many people. Or someone who has suffered grave injustice. Or a man that nobody loves. Thank God I don't know anyone who has ever done anything truly bad."

"I know one," I said.

"Who's that?"

"An artist. A draftsman."

"What did he do?"

I felt a sort of stagefright, having now to tell an incident to the great storyteller.

It happened that some young friends and I had once had a great carousal on New Year's Eve. It was eight in the morning when we went home, singing, through the snow-covered streets. We had drunk a good deal, and were bound and determined to do some sort of mischief. As we were going along, we caught sight of a mailbox from whose slot the corner of a white envelope stuck out. Just before New Year's so many greeting cards are mailed that the boxes are all jammed. That was what had happened to this mailbox. The envelope whose corner stuck out would not quite go into the jammed box. The young man in question, a draftsman, pulled the letter out. The envelopes of New Year's cards are usually not sealed. He drew out the card, which showed a winter landscape with a name perfectly strange to us printed below, and under the printed name the following in fine, careful, mercantile handwriting: "Wishes a Happy New Year to his esteemed chief." On the envelope was the name of the chief, also unknown to us, and the address of a great bank. Plainly the sender was a dutiful bank clerk.

We went to a café. The draftsman asked for pen and ink. His specialty was imitating anyone's writing to perfection (which incidentally is a sign that he was a good draftsman). He took the pen, made a few trials on another piece of paper, and then transformed the period after the poor bank clerk's sentence into a comma, and continued the sentence as follows: . . . "warning him that if he continues to treat his subordinates with such stupidity and injustice in the New Year as he did in the last, it will come to a bad end." The forgery was perfect. The draftsman put the card back into the envelope, and dropped the envelope in the mailbox again. That was all.

"A malicious trick," said the Captain.

"More than a trick," I said. "Imagine the perfectly endless vistas resulting from that one prank. What disaster, grief, and suffering may have resulted!"

And I recited them:

1. The pained surprise of the chief when he received the card.

2. The first encounter between the chief and the unsuspecting clerk.

3. The painful dilemma of the chief, wondering whether he should mention the matter to his subordinate.

4. A possibility: the chief did not say a word, but let him feel his anger for the rest of his life.

5. A possibility: the chief mentioned the card to him. The horrified protest of the subordinate that he never wrote any such thing.

6. The moment when the chief showed him the card, and he read the terrible lines.

7. Did the chief believe him when he swore that he was not the one who had written the second half of the sentence?

8. Would the chief accuse him of falsehood because of it?

9. If not, then the agonized wondering of the chief and the clerk: who did write it? Who had written it?

10. The clerk's sleepless night, the insoluble puzzle. He himself had dropped the envelope in the mailbox; only the mailman could have removed it. Had the mailman written the words?

11. The chief's suspicion that the clerk was crazy.

12. The chief's suspicion that the clerk had written the greeting while drunk.

13. The chief's painful reflection: "If I believe him that someone else wrote those insulting words, then who is this secret enemy of mine?"

14. Where did the forgery take place? In the clerk's home? The painful thought of the clerk: who was this secret enemy in his family?

15. Where did the forgery take place? At the chief's house after the card had arrived? The chief's worry: "Who is this scoundrel in my house? Not my son, with whom I had a quarrel last week?"

16. The suspicion of the chief: perhaps there was no forgery, and instead the clerk had made a bet with someone that he would tell the chief the truth for New Year's.

17. And most grievous of all, the sure effect of the card on the chief's spirit, because he would unfailingly begin to wrestle with the question of whether he actually treated his subordinates stupidly and unjustly.

"You could go on with that for a long time," I said, "because this was a pure piece of hundred-percent malice, because it was absolutely disinterested."

"There was an excuse," said the Captain. "You were all drunk."

"No," I replied, "the draftsman was the only one of us who had not touched a drop."

Chapter VIII

ONE EVENING THE CAPTAIN CAME INTO MY ROOM, bringing along a bottle of cognac.

"I can't heat my room," he said. "My stove burst from being heated too hot, and it hasn't been repaired yet."

My room was nice and warm.

From the cracked marble top of the washstand he took two water glasses, which he filled with cognac. "I'm in a bad humor," he said. "The lady has really taken me in in great style."

The "lady" was Mercedes, the black-haired actress-to-be.

I maintained discreet silence.

"She's constantly deceiving me. She sends for me, and then isn't at home. She spends all her time with that lame fellow; Pharmaco spied on her as a favor. They always eat supper in a dirty dump up on the mountain. I can't see that. He's a sallow, ugly, tubercular man. He's the booking agent at some kind of a stand in the amusement park with a vaudeville program. The lady explains her behavior by saying that this fellow will get her an engagement in Paris, at the Folies Bergères. It's perfectly extraordinary how wretched creatures like him influence women. Of course Paris is just waiting for her!"

He took a great gulp of cognac. "He leads her around by the nose; all my efforts are futile." He looked at me piercingly. "Look here . . . you knew that I'm not an active officer?"

"So I had heard."

"You heard correctly. I resigned. You didn't know that I'm not really allowed to wear this uniform?"

"Yes, I did know."

"And I wear it anyhow. Not always. Only when the fit takes me. I don't care if they lock me up or draw and quarter me. I can't part with this remnant of my hussarhood. It would make me ill if I didn't wear it now and then." He pondered for some time. "Tell me," he said softly, "you live under the same roof with me, you know that I am out of the army, yet you aren't curious to know why?"

"Of course I am."

"Then why do you never ask?"

"I didn't think it would be suitable."

His eyes flashed severely at me. "What? Surely you don't think I did anything improper?"

"Heaven forfend!"

"Well, then."

Reassured, he drank. I wondered what he could be living on. Nobody knew. Sometimes he had money, sometimes not.

"Well," he said, "it began with the Jews. I've

been fond of two Jews in my life. One was the proprietor of the Café Mirabella, the other Lieutenant Rado, whose name was Roth, but when he became an active officer he changed his name to Rado, which sounded Hungarian. He was a thin, dark Jew boy, silent, punctual, orderly, a very good soldier. He stayed in the army because the officers liked him, and urged him to stay in the army when his year's service was up. Even though he was a Jew. But first I'll tell you quickly the story about the proprietor of the Café Mirabella. He was an elderly Jew. And you can write this one—not the one about Rado. Do you know where the Café Mirabella is?"

"In the Andrassy ut."

"Right. In a big, four-story corner building. They say it used to belong to another Jew by the name of Pollak. Well, one afternoon a Polish Jew with a beard and a long black caftan comes into this Pollak's Café Mirabella. The Mirabella was full of women in silks, drinking coffee. The man in the caftan sat down in the extreme corner at a small table, and waited. The waiter must have gone past ten times, but never asked what he wanted.

"Finally he called the waiter: 'A cup of coffee, please.' The waiter looked at him, and said, 'We haven't any coffee.' The man in the caftan looked at him wide-eyed. What, no coffee in a big café like that? He was beginning to suspect that they did not want to serve him because they were ashamed of his caftan in front of all the other, fashionable Jews.

"Going over to the cashier's desk, where the proprietor was standing, he greeted him civilly and inquired, 'If you please, is it true what the waiter tells me, that there isn't any coffee here?' The proprietor looked at him disdainfully, and said: 'Not for you.'

" 'Thank you,' said the man in the caftan, and went out. It was raining outside; that's important too. He stood in the rain outside the fashionable café for a while, and his heart ached. I know that, because he told me so himself. His heart ached because the Jewish café-owner was ashamed of him on account of the Jewish guests. 'If it had been an anti-Semite,' he said, 'I wouldn't have said a word.'

"He stood outside the café for a while, then went into the building and asked the doorman where the owner of the building lived. He lived on the second floor. He went up to see him. He told me they discussed the matter for about an hour.

"After an hour they telephoned a lawyer, for the man in the caftan had bought the building. He paid the full purchase price on the spot and then went downstairs with the lawyer to the café, and gave the proprietor notice. The proprietor was so astonished by the whole story that it was not until an hour later in the gambling room that he fainted away.

"This was about eight years ago; since that time the other man has owned the café, and has doubled his fortune. You can write the story, but make the title 'Anger Is a Bad Counselor.'

"I grew very fond of the fellow. There's a man for you. For years I went to the café every night, and we used to drink our brandy together. I used to make him tell me the story every week because it was such a wonderful one. Only I did feel sorry that he took to wearing a gray English tweed suit and a red tie. He really ought never to have taken off his caftan. But that's none of my business now. I mentioned it because he's one of my Jews."

"And Rado?"

"The other one. He did play a part in my life, the poor fellow. Rado was not a hussar, but an infantryman. But he was in the same town of Nagyvarad where I was. I used to sit with him a lot in the café; not so much in the restaurant. He was an excellent chess player. Well, if you please, down in Dalmatia or somewhere in one of those wild regions, they were having maneuvers. And the following business happened to Rado. During the maneuvers, that is, on duty as a lieutenant, he was going through some big woods, and after him his orderly, an honest Hungarian lad. They walked and walked, and then sat down to rest on some big stones or rocks.

"As they were sitting there, Rado's striker suddenly began to yell, because a viper had bitten him. They tell me the whole country is full of vipers down there. The boy yelled, and Rado was in a terrible fright, because he knew that one of these viper bites is deadly. The snake had caught the boy on the upper thigh, where it could reach him as he sat, deep under his hip. Notice that, because it's important too. Under the hip. A small patrol of officers came by, and they heard what had happened, but nobody could help. The poor fellow was yelling, because he too had heard that you could die of it. Several of them said you had to suck the blood out of the wound right away, and no harm would happen.

"Well, who was ready to do that? Nobody. Rado was very fond of the boy. That hardly needs mentioning; it's usually the way. Well, who was willing? Nobody was willing. They actually even smiled. Finally Rado forced himself to suck the blood from the poisoned bite. A hundred doctors afterward said that he saved his striker's life by doing it. It was in a bad place, as I told you—on the upper part of the thigh. The results in the town of Nagyvarad were most unfortunate. The officers said they wouldn't sit at the same table with Rado. You know how it usually is in a provincial town. The whole town knew about it. There was so much gossip that the officers' corps had to take up the case.

"And I can't blame those officers; from their standpoint they were perfectly right. No officer could go around among the enlisted men when he had kissed a buck private's backside, even if it was from the side. It was a disastrous situation.

"The officers were right, and poor Rado was right too. But I was young then, and very indignant at the strict orthodoxy of the officers. I had very acrimonious arguments with them, and even with my brother officers in the cavalry.

"Rado was nowhere to be found; he went to Budapest, for he was ashamed to be seen. I kept exposing myself more and more—you know, I had charged into it and got tangled up in it; in those days I still believed a fellow like Rado might shoot himself if he had to resign from the army. On his account I was at outs with everybody, and went to dinner alone for weeks. I couldn't do him any good. Rado was given to understand that he must immediately resign his commission and get out of the army, and within a month the affair was forgotten. The only thing not forgotten was that I had savagely upheld the opposite point of view, and now my position began to be untenable. Secretly the whole regiment became my enemies. I had a friend—I won't mention his name—a lieutenant of hussars, with whom I was sharing a room. He began urging me to get myself transferred; and then the disaster happened."

At the word disaster his face was distorted for an instant. It was a bitter, scornful grimace, dissolving into a smile. "Take a drink," he said. "The real part is coming now."

I drank and listened.

Chapter IX

"THIS LIEUTENANT THAT I LIVED WITH," THE CAPtain went on, "was the most charming hussar in the world. Just to show you what a charming boy he was—he and his twin brother, who was just as charming—I'll tell you how the two fooled a lot of Budapest barbers, although that doesn't really belong in this story. They were twins, and as much alike as two peas in a pod. Furthermore they were both hussars, both lieutenants. Their regiments were in two cities some distance apart. They were very fond of each other, and whenever they got leave, they would go to Budapest to spend their leave together. On these trips they would intentionally arrive unshaven in Budapest, with two days' beard, and one of them would go straight to a barber and get a shave. Then he would leave the barber shop.

"Ten minutes later his twin brother, the other lieutenant, would come into the same barber shop and sit down in the barber chair to get his two days' growth of beard shaved off. The barber almost fainted with fright. It was the greatest surprise of his life—a man whose beard grew in ten minutes. They used to repeat this on every occasion, and always with another barber.

"But as I say, that wasn't what I meant to talk about. My friend, one of the twins, was a good-hearted, brave lad, as innocent in the ways of the world as a ten-year-old girl. He was handsome, jolly, fond of a drink, and—this is important—the most passionate cardplayer I ever knew. There was no great difference in ages between us, but still I was always a bit of a father to him, if only for the reason that I used to be a much steadier fellow. I wanted a great military career. Now, it's all the same . . .

"Let's get on with it. The boy gambled like a madman, and always lost. He was up to his ears in debt. By this time I had stopped admonishing him so much not to play, because I thought after all he was bound to win some day, and then he could pay off his moneylenders. But he went on losing. We lived together in a room with two beds. I was usually long since asleep when he came home at night—or rather in the morning—red with champagne and losses, and on starting up from my dreams I would see him toss a few crumpled banknotes in the drawer of his bedside table, take off his clothes, and get into bed.

"Sometimes I asked him, 'Well?' The answer was always the same, 'Lost.' I was in despair over him.

"Then I happened to think of an idea. I had it! I decided that every time he fell asleep drunk like this I would put away some of the banknotes he threw uncounted into the drawer—after all, he never knew how much money he brought home—save up the money for him, and some fine day when it had become a nice round sum, I would hand him the money and tell him how I had saved it for him. And so I did.

"At that time the boy was getting an average of two hours' sleep a day, for he would hardly be home before he had to go on duty. He used to sleep like a log the moment he fell into bed. Then I would wait a couple of minutes, reach out my hand to the bedside table that stood between the two beds, gently pull out the drawer, and, judging by weight how much it was, I would take out a few banknotes and put them in my own drawer. This went on for weeks. He never noticed anything missing.

"But one night as usual he came home toward morning, and began to undress. He put a fistful of crumpled money into the drawer. I woke up, and said, 'Well?' He said bitterly, 'Won.' By that time I had already collected a nice little fortune for him. I don't know how late it was; the point is dawn was just breaking, and there was the least bit of light in the room. He lay down and fell asleep.

"I waited until he began to breathe deeply and regularly, and then I reached slowly for his drawer. Then I pushed the drawer back, and, lying in bed as I was in the very faint twilight, I looked to see how much I had happened to take.

"Sitting there holding the money, I suddenly noticed that the rhythm of his breathing had changed. I had a cold feeling in my chest. Turning my head slowly toward him, I could see that he was not asleep. His head lay quiet on the pillow, but his eyes were wide open, looking at me. My first thought was that he was dead, so fixedly, so mutely and breathlessly, was he gazing at me.

"I looked into his eyes. That took a long time. Then I spoke to him softly. He answered.

"The conversation was this: 'Are you awake?'

" 'Yes,' he answered. I lit the light, with the money in my hand.

" 'Well,' I said to him, 'you don't say anything.'

" 'No,' he said softly, and very sadly. I sat up in bed and began to ponder, the banknotes in my hand. Of late he had often asked me: 'How is it that you manage to distribute your money so wisely? We're all up to our necks in debt, and you don't owe anybody a penny.' Was I to start now explaining to him that I had stolen the money out of his drawer every night for him? Now I know that my hesitation was fatally stupid, yet in that situation to this day I would still swear to you that in his place I would

never have believed the fairy tale of the clever friend
trying to help the gambler. The idea was improper
in itself, and it brought its own punishment.

"Then it was too late. If he had at least yelled at
me! It was agonizing to see how he kept looking at
me; surely he must have seen the whole business of
the drawer, and even when our eyes did meet, he
still said nothing, but simply looked at me with deep
sadness.

"So I turned to him and said, 'Look here, I tell
you on my word of honor as an officer that I have
been taking money out of your drawer every night
and saving it up here in my drawer for you, so that
when I got enough of it I could surprise you with
it.' Then I opened my drawer and showed him the
money.

" 'Wonderful,' he said, but his smile was not genu-
ine. I took the pile of banknotes out of my drawer,
and put it on his bedside table. 'There,' I said, 'that's
how much it is so far.'

"He made no answer. He smiled. I ask you, what
was to be done? Nothing.

"My drawer was still open. I reached in calmly,
and took out my revolver. That was blunder num-
ber two. But in those days I could not do anything
else. Of course he promptly flung himself upon me
and wrested the revolver from me. This was just
when I was most unpopular on account of Rado.

"A week later I threw up my commission. You

were right not to ask why I got out. I might never have told you if you had. As it is, I did tell it, as you see. That's how it happened, my boy."

He was weary of talking. His face wore an almost tragic expression. Getting up, he took a large swallow of cognac, lit a cigarette, and walked silently to and fro in the little room. For my part I knelt down before the little stove, and crammed in all the wood I could. Possibly I did it automatically, because at that time I had been reading a great many Russian novels, and in Russian novels whenever the storyteller has finished his tale, the flames in the stove are usually dying away, only the glowing coals gleam red, and just then somebody in the deep silence usually "tosses a few sticks of wood upon the coals in the stove."

And now I must divulge a confidence to the reader, something that I have so far made the mistake of not telling.

The fact is that the Captain had never been an officer in his life. He was a mystifier, an adventurer through and through. Later it turned out that he had once done service as a private in the infantry.

The story about Rado may have been true, quite independently of him. He had surely heard it somewhere. The case of the proprietor of the Mirabella Café, was, as I later learned, a well-known story. I later heard of a similar occurrence that was supposed to have taken place in New York. Possibly the story of the Mirabella man had been transplanted from Budapest to New York, but it is also possible that America had exported the story to Budapest. Nor is it altogether out of the question for it to have happened twice. There are examples of that too. The "Story of Two Friends" may, according to a conviction that I have often reconsidered but always clung to, actually have happened; in fact when I think back on his way of telling it, I believe it did happen to him, only not as an officer and not in exactly those circumstances.

And my mistake of not telling that he had never been an officer was intentional, and due to the consideration that when he told me these things I myself was firmly and unshakably convinced of his captaincy.

Chapter X

I DIDN'T SEE HIM FOR SEVERAL DAYS. HE DID NOT come back to the hotel. It had happened before that he would disappear in this way; but now, with the chapter that he had just contributed to his biography having such a tragic background, I was a little uneasy on his account. And he was so desperately in love, too. I considered it probable that he was devoting himself to drink.

I went around town to a few cafés where I knew he was in the habit of going, and inquired of the headwaiters. Finally I got news of him at the Café Cairo. He had been there the evening before, alone.

"Drinking?" I asked.

"Was he!" said the headwaiter. "He ordered three bottles of Pommery champagne, but it wasn't he that paid for them."

"Who was it?"

"A Mr. Fur-Coat."

"Who?"

"Mr. Fur-Coat."

I stared stupidly at him, and he smiled stupidly back at me. I then learned the following. The Captain had appeared after dinner at the Café Cairo, already having had a few plum brandies, and sat down at a small table against the wall with two chairs. He sat down on one chair, and put his fur coat carefully on the other, turning the fur lining outward. He had a new and expensive fur coat. It was a regulation military greatcoat, but the fur lining was finer and more costly than in other fur coats. I knew that he was fond and proud of this fur coat.

The Café Cairo was crowded. When the Captain put his coat on the chair, and ordered strong coffee, the headwaiter said politely: "Captain, will you please check your coat?"

"I'm not going to," he replied, "it will be stolen."

"It won't be stolen," said the headwaiter, offended, "and besides, the Café is financially responsible for all articles checked." He reached for the fur coat to take it off to the checkroom.

The Captain looked at him savagely, and sharply rebuked him, "Put it back on the chair. It isn't true at all that I'm afraid the coat might be stolen. I love my new fur coat, and want to keep on looking at it."

The startled headwaiter put the coat back on the chair, but said briskly, "This chair is not there for a coat to lie on, but for a patron to sit in."

"Now, now!" cried the Captain. "Does that make much difference?"

"Yes," said the headwaiter. "Particularly now, after the theatre, when the café is crowded and new patrons keep coming in. If a guest sits in that chair, he'll order something."

"I tell you what," said the Captain, "bring my fur coat a cup of strong coffee too."

The headwaiter was taken aback. This was something he had not been prepared for. He could make no objection to the retort. He went and brought two cups of coffee on two trays. One for the captain, one for the fur coat.

The Captain turned politely to the coat. "Dear friend, how much sugar will you have in your coffee?" He held his ear to the collar of the fur coat, like someone listening for an answer. Thereupon he put two lumps of sugar into the fur coat's coffee. The guests at the neighboring tables laughed loudly. The headwaiter, reddening with fury, went to the other end of the café.

But soon he was back. "Captain," he said, "that was a joke, but enough is enough. Supposing a guest had sat in that chair, how do you know he would just have ordered coffee, and not a bottle of wine or some sort of French liqueur that would have brought the café more profit than one cup of coffee?"

The guests at the neighboring tables listened eagerly. In the general silence the Captain spoke up. "Very well. I'm drinking coffee myself, because that's my habit at this time of day. But you can bring Mr. Fur-Coat a bottle of champagne, and make it Pommery & Greno Extra Dry, vintage 1898, because that's what he's accustomed to. And glasses."

After a few moments a bottle of Pommery stood before the coat, and the Captain said to the guests who sat at the tables around, "Mr. Fur-Coat is in high spirits today because he has succeeded in putting to shame a crass-minded headwaiter. That's why he is drinking champagne and inviting you to drink with him."

Glasses came, and everyone drank. The Captain put a large banknote on the table in front of the fur coat, and said, "Mr. Fur-Coat wishes to order another bottle of Pommery."

This also was brought. Then a third. All the neighbors drank too, and one of them proposed a toast to the generous Mr. Fur-Coat. The ladies smiled their loveliest smiles at the Captain. After an hour or so the money lying before the fur coat was exhausted. The Captain motioned to the headwaiter. "The check, please."

Mr. Fur-Coat paid the whole bill, with a large tip. The Captain thrust the change from the banknote into the pocket of the fur coat, and got up. The headwaiter, reconciled by now, rushed up obsequiously to the fur coat, and was about to help the Captain put it on.

"Wait a minute!" roared the Captain. "How dare you treat this distinguished guest as if he were an ordinary garment? Send for two people, have a third man take hold of him, and don't have him put on me, but have me put into Mr. Fur-Coat."

And so in fact they did. Two waiters picked up the Captain from the floor, and slid him slowly into the fur coat, which the headwaiter held up in the air. The Captain left the establishment amid thunderous applause. The patrons told the headwaiter that this was a better show than the one they had just come from.

This last sentence was not particularly to my liking, because the Café Cairo was in the immediate vicinity of the theatre where a play of mine was running.

Chapter XI

READER, IF YOU ARE NEITHER A GAMBLER NOR A doctor, you can skip this chapter. I can't leave it out, because I consider it essential to the biography of the Captain. It explains, renders comprehensive and excusable, some of his actions, his now and then incomprehensible behavior, not only from the psychological but also from the pathological standpoint.

As we know, the Captain by this time was a passionate gambler. He played cards a great deal, not only on St. Margaret's Island, but in the back rooms of cafés, and especially in the "clubs" tolerated by the police that had roulette tables after the Monte Carlo fashion. He was a good gambler. Sometimes I would spend a whole night sitting silent beside him admiring his daring inspirations and his sometimes perfectly diabolical instinct. Like all really gifted gamblers, if he managed to catch luck by the collar after a few slight vacillations during the first fifteen minutes, he would never let go for the rest of the evening.

One day he came to me and said he was having some sort of trouble with his stomach. He had had some doctor examine him. The result of the examination was not at all encouraging. The doctor told him there was nothing wrong with his stomach, but advised him to have himself examined at once by a nerve specialist. Both of us were laymen sufficiently experienced to have forebodings. A stomach ailment in which the doctor is curious not so much about the stomach as about knee, pupil, and other reflexes is likely to be a serious matter.

"I don't care," he said, "I'll have myself examined. This hydropathic doctor of ours is a nerve specialist. The fact that he's contending with financial embarrassments doesn't necessarily prove he's not a good doctor. Come up with me while I see him. I don't like to go to doctors alone."

We went up to the Doctor's office on the third floor. The Captain was instructed to strip naked and submit to the ceremonies usual with nerve specialists. He had to walk with eyes closed, touch the middle finger of his right hand with the middle finger of his left, and so on and so forth. He succeeded in this, more or less. Then came the most important examination, which I had heard of, but never seen. The Captain was required to lie down naked on his stomach on the couch. The Doctor produced a long pin, a regular, sharp hatpin with a knob at the other end. By this means specialists are in the habit of testing whether the nerves of the back react properly. The test consists in the doctor's touching the back of the patient, who lies on his stomach, now with the point of the pin, now with the knob; the patient cannot see the pin, and is supposed to say whether the point or the knob has touched his bare skin. The Doctor explained this, and then the examination began. First the Doctor touched the Captain's back with the point of the pin.

"Point," said the Captain.

"Good," said the Doctor, touching his skin with the point of the hatpin.

"Point again," said the Captain.

"Good," said the Doctor. "And now?"

"Point again."

"Very good. And now?"

"Point again."

"Good."

This time he touched him with the head.

"Head," said the Captain.

"And now?"

"Point."

"Very good."

And so it went. The Doctor touched him eight or ten times with the hatpin, and always the Captain told him whether it was point or head. He never missed once. I heaved a sigh of relief. The anxious feeling that had oppressed me during the whole examination passed off. I was in good spirits as I went downstairs with him.

In the lobby he suddenly spoke. "My boy, I'm a very sick man."

I looked at him in astonishment.

"Yes, yes," he said. "My case is very serious."

"What do you mean?" I cried. "The examination was a great success! I was afraid at first, but when I saw how splendidly you told each time whether the hatpin—"

"My dear friend," he said with a melancholy smile, "I swear to you that I never knew once whether the point of the needle or the head was against my back. The first time he touched me I got it into my head that if anyone is making an examination with a pin, the point of the pin will occur to him first, because the essence of a pin is its point and not its head. Then the doctor made a mistake. When I answered his question I said 'Point,' and he said, 'Good.' It flashed through my mind that actually I was gambling on a two-way chance, because there are two possibilities about a pin—point and head. It's like roulette at Monte Carlo, or anywhere else —*rouge* and *noir*. Now that's something I really know about, but more than that, I've been playing in great luck for weeks. When he touched me the second time with the pin, I gambled on 'point' again, and he said, 'Good.' At that the delicious feeling ran through me that takes possession of a gambler when he can feel that this is his lucky day. I played 'point' again and again, until I felt that the run was over, and 'head' would come up next. I won again. I simply won eight or ten stakes in succession, as if I had been playing red and black in roulette—which is not difficult, and nothing uncommon. It has happened at the club that I would win at roulette fifteen times running. If that hydropathic donkey had held his tongue after each touch, I would have been in a predicament."

It will be hard for me ever to forget his smile, described above as "melancholy," for it was something different and far more than melancholy.

Chapter XII

THE FOLLOWING MORNING AT NINE THE CAPTAIN came banging at my door. He did this often, although he knew I was in the habit of going to bed at six in the morning. He sat down beside me.

"I told you recently that I had loved two Jews. I was wrong. I have loved three."

"And for that you waked me out of the midst of my dreams?"

"For that. The third one's name was Schurz. He was an old man. His profession was that of usurer."

"And you loved him? A usurer?"

"Very much."

"And . . . is that all?"

"No. I've got to explain why I loved him. I'm no anti-Semite, but when it's a question of a Jew a cavalry officer always has to explain why he's fond of him. There are Jews, though of course only a few, whom even our Imperial and Royal Majesty loves. But he always makes it a practice to say why. It's strange, but it's so; I can't help it.

"Just once I said something mildly disagreeable to a Jew, and was sorry afterward even for that. In case you're interested, it was my godchild. An honest, thirty-year-old bank clerk. He got himself baptized, adopted the Catholic faith, and chose me for his godfather.

"On the day before the ceremony he came to call on me, and asked: 'Will I be properly dressed if I go to church to be baptized tomorrow in a cutaway and dark striped trousers?'

" 'Right,' I told him.

" 'What sort of shoes should I wear?' he asked.

"I said, 'That I can't tell you, my boy, because I was barefoot when they baptized me.'

"But let's get back to old Schurz. As aforesaid, old Schurz was a usurer. In my opinion usurers are benefactors of humanity, and especially of the cavalry. You needn't gape at me like that. A cavalry officer has two indispensable attributes: his horse and his financial difficulties. Friends who occasionally help out a person with small loans are simply doctors prescribing a powder for a headache. Usurers—now there are the great surgeons, saving our lives with a major operation. I repeat for the third time, old Schurz was a usurer.

"I was a cardplayer by then. Schurz lived in the town of Arad, because a regiment of hussars was garrisoned there. A thoroughbred usurer loves neither the infantry nor the artillery. Only the cavalry. He not only lends money to the officers, but takes care of their other affairs.

"In general we took him for a decent fellow. The officers not only loved him, they trusted him. This went so far that when an officer was transferred to some other town, no matter where Fate sent him, he would continue to be a client of old Schurz for years. Some people, who wanted to be witty at all costs, called him Shylock. I always regarded that as base ingratitude.

"About that time I was transferred from Arad to Budapest. Here, of course, I played cards more than ever. I lost, and was in acute financial distress.

"I had a valuable old family ring, and decided to sell it. Obviously no one else but old Schurz was to be thought of. The matter was very pressing. I took the old ring, put it in its little old red leather case, wrapped it up, and sent it by mail with a short, categorical note to old Schurz at Arad.

"I wrote: 'Enclosed I send you my old family ring. If you want to give three thousand crowns for it, keep it. If you don't want to give that much, send the ring back at once. I won't take a penny less. No haggling.' Then I waited for an answer.

"In two days I got a telegram. Contrary to my instructions, old Schurz tried to bargain. He wired: 'Ring not worth three thousand. Give two thousand at most.'

"Furiously I answered: 'Price of ring three thousand. No haggling.'

"The next day came another telegram. The old fox went on bargaining: 'Offer twenty-five hundred, positively no more.'

"At this I lost patience, and wired: 'Ring three thousand. No haggling. Return immediately.'

"A few days passed, and I got a little package by mail from: Schurz. Contents: ring. I opened the parcel. There lay the case with the ring, carefully tied up and sealed. On top of the case was a note from old Schurz—to my annoyance, more haggling, as follows: 'As an expert I tell you that this ring is not worth three thousand crowns. You would never get that much for it anywhere in the world. However, because I like you, I raise my last offer from twenty-five hundred to twenty-eight hundred crowns. That is my final word. If you want to sell for that price, don't open the case, just send it back to me as is. I will send the money the following day. If you don't want to sell the ring even for twenty-eight hundred, keep your ring; I wouldn't buy it.'

"I was deeply embittered on reading this. I vowed I would not sell the ring any cheaper, would not send it back, and would try to sell it to someone else.

"Exasperated, I broke the seal and opened the red leather case. The ring was not there. In its place was a tiny paper with the following words: 'All right, all right, don't get excited, I will give you three thousand crowns.'"

I had almost fallen asleep in the middle of the story, but at this unexpected conclusion I awoke.

"How can one help loving a man like that?" said the Captain in a tone of honest enthusiasm.

"Love him?" I asked sleepily. "Well, no. At most I might admire him."

"You're in a bad humor," he said, "because you need sleep. I'm not surprised at a time like this that you can't see how fine it is for a person in a cruel occupation—this usurer, for example—to be able to treat his victim kindly."

He gave me a suspicious yet fatherly look.

"Where were you all night? I hear you got in at six-thirty. I make no doubt you were rehearsing some pretty actress the whole time."

I was irritable, and my patience gave way. I yelled angrily at him: "Do stop constantly suspecting me of idle trifling! If you must know, this morning at dawn I was studying that very subject of how a person in a cruel occupation can be kind to his victim."

"Another usurer?"

"No," I yelled, "a hangman!"

He looked at me in amazement, thinking I was having a bad joke.

"Yes, that's it," I said. "What I was doing a few hours ago was studying not a pretty actress, but Michael Bali, the official Hungarian hangman."

This was in fact the case. The evening before, my editor-in-chief had given me the far from pleasant assignment of attending as a reporter at the Central Prison, where the aforesaid Michael Bali was to hang a condemned murderer at five in the morning. Up to four-thirty I was actually rehearsing a young actress in a part that she was to take in my one-act cabaret play. I went with my credentials to the Central Prison at half past four. In the prison yard I took my place among the other reporters to await the hanging; I was chagrined to have been assigned a place directly beside the gallows.

Shortly after five the condemned man was led in. It was a dreadfully cold, pitch black morning. Two bright electric lights lit up the little prison yard. One light shone on a table at which the members of the court sat down. The unfortunate victim was brought before the court, and the state's attorney read out the death sentence, adding that His Majesty the King had refused his appeal for a pardon.

The state's attorney was a black-bearded, formidable man with somberly sparkling eyes. If all this had been not terrible reality, but a shocker in a theatre, undoubtedly he would have taken the part of the hangman instead of the real executioner, Mr. Michael Bali, who was a gentle old peasant with a gray mustache and a kindly, nay fatherly expression on his face.

The condemned man was taken from the terrible state's attorney to the kindly hangman. Old Bali was standing near me, beside the gallows, with the rope in his hand. As the culprit, a young man, stood up before the executioner, he smiled sadly and said, "Good morning, Uncle Michael."

The executioner replied, "Good morning, my sweet son." This is a special Hungarian form of address; parents call their sons "sweet son." The hangman's assistants tied the condemned man's hands behind his back, helped him up the three steps to the little platform at the gallows, and there bound his feet as well. Old Michael Bali mounted the platform and lifted the rope to put it around the victim's neck.

At that moment the condemned man smiled at the gentle old hangman again and said softly to him, "You won't forget what you promised me, will you, Uncle Michael, that you'd do it in the 'special way'?"

"Never fear, my sweet son," the hangman told him, "I'll do it the way I promised you—that's my specialty. You'll see that it won't hurt, and will be over in a second."

"Thank you, Uncle Michael," said the condemned man.

"Not at all," replied Uncle Michael, quickly hanging his sweet son. How he did it, and what the pleasant specialty that he had promised might have been, I missed seeing, for at the last moment I looked away. After the execution, when the doctor had announced that the condemned man was dead, and while Uncle Michael was distributing little bits of the rope as souvenirs to the reporters, I asked him what this specialty of his might be.

"That's my secret," he said, "which I don't give away except to the people I hang. But so far they've all been pleased, poor fellows, when I promised them."

The Captain listened to my account with a gloomy countenance.

"Well," I said, "what is the amiability of your usurer against that of Uncle Michael? Uncle Michael is the one you can't help loving, not your old fellow."

"There's nothing new about that," he said thoughtfully. "In China the relatives of the condemned man usually pay the executioner a heavy bribe to behead the victim with a sword heated red hot. That doesn't hurt at all."

"How do you know it doesn't hurt?" I asked.

"It's a dead certainty that it doesn't hurt," he said quite without conviction, going out of the room and slamming the door.

Chapter XIII

THAT SAME DAY AFTER LUNCH, BEFORE THE CAP-
tain went into town—God knows where or why
—I met him in the hotel. I was weary and worn out
because I went to bed in the morning, and he had
awakened me at nine o'clock with his ring story, and
I was unable to get to sleep again. I was nervous and
out of temper. I envied him for his ability to be
walking briskly around the hotel by eight or nine
o'clock, for he too used to come home late in the
morning.

I accosted him, "Tell me, don't you ever sleep?"

"The idea!" he said. "You go to bed in the morning yourself."

"Yes. But if I don't sleep until afternoon, I'm a
wreck all day. You come home at seven, and by
nine you are breakfasting in the restaurant and
arguing the beauties of life with Baron Kalotay.
This very moment you're as fresh as young lettuce."

"There's a special secret about that," he said, "or
rather there are special secrets about it."

"Tell me what they are," I said. "I need them.
Newspapering is night work, and I often have business early in the morning."

"Listen carefully," he said, "because this is the
assembled experience of a stormy life."

"Shall I get out my notebook?"

"That would be the best way. If only because my biography would be incomplete without it. Put down that mankind spends a third of its life asleep. A man of eighty has slept away about twenty-seven years. It's dreadful to spend so much of this lovely, interesting, and brief life of ours unconscious. There are many people in the world who refuse to be reconciled to this, partly because they love life, partly because they have a great deal to do. Such people should learn how to outwit Nature."

"Master," I cried, "teach us how not to sleep!" I sharpened my pencil.

"Sleep," he said, "has many forms, that is to say, many substitutes. You need not necessarily sleep in the same way as other people. For instance you can sleep by way of the razor."

"How so?"

"When you come home in the morning and shave *at once*, carefully and closely, it will take the place of an hour's sleep, because afterward you feel as much fresher as if you had slept for an hour."

"Thank you," said I, feverishly taking notes.

The Captain went on, "Clean collar, putting on a fresh, cold, starched collar, half an hour's sleep. But a complete change, a clean, cool shirt, smelling of the laundry, crackling as you put it on, not yet shaped to your body, is as good as three hours' sleep. Washing, half an hour. Complete cold bath, two hours. An ice-cold or very hot bath takes the place of three hours' sleep. So if you go home, bathe, and change, that means you've gained six or seven hours. But the collar wants to be stiff, not soft."

"Yes."

"Coming home and finding some annoyance, for instance a registered letter from a lawyer saying you must pay up or else, is as good as half an hour's sleep. Any annoyance refreshes you, driving half an hour's sleepiness from your eyes. In general, bad news will take the place of an hour's sleep. Good news makes you sleepy. Leaving home at once will take the place of half an hour's sleep. If you stay home, you get sleepy."

"Yes."

"Strong eau de cologne is a good thing. Chafing your face, neck, chest and hands briskly, three-quarters of an hour. Repeated brutal scratching of your scalp while combing your hair, fifteen minutes' sleep. Do that several times during the day. A large breakfast with very strong black coffee, four hours' sleep. All further cups of black coffee, a quarter-hour each. I can sleep more than an hour after lunch, by drinking four cups of black coffee and combing my hair hard. Believe me, it's so refreshing that you feel like a new man. It's a good thing to have the comb made of metal."

"Yes."

"Pushing your eyes back hard into their sockets with the heel of your hand, ten minutes' sleep. You can sleep wonderfully in society like that. I once slept until I was completely rested while at a ball, and everyone around me was tired and sleepy.

"Let's go on. Not drinking anything alcoholic after spending a night awake, an hour's sleep. At times like that walking is bad. Sit down a lot, don't stand, and don't lie down. Don't smoke cigars— nothing but cigarettes, but smoke them one after another. Drink your water iced. As little physical work as possible, and as much mental work.

"Two things more. Don't read anything tiresome. Political editorials will make you fall right out of your chair. If you do read, choose your reading matter well: don't pick anything that you enjoy, but something that provokes you beyond measure. Read bad but popular authors who get an outrageous amount of money for each story. Or read great poets of whom it is generally known that they starved to death. Either one is as good as a cup of black coffee.

"That's one point. The other is, don't go back to the place where you had been staying awake, because your eyes will immediately become glued shut. If you go there, it will occur to you that everyone else has gone to bed and is now sleeping sweetly. This thought can make a man terribly sleepy."

"Yes."

"Avoid women at times like this, although those are the very occasions when you long for them more than otherwise. But at such times a woman is poison. When you leave her, you will fall asleep at once."

"Yes, Master."

"A headache is fine. Excellent. A headache will take the place of an hour and a half's sleep. Accordingly, don't take any aspirin or other powder. Avoid anything that might calm, soothe, or satisfy you. If you play cards on a day like this, play with poor players who make you furious by their stupidity. Don't win; lose. Heavy losses at cards will often replace several hours' sleep. Don't pay off any debts on one of these days. It makes you sleepy. Don't call on any friend you haven't seen for a long time. Look up your old mistress somewhere, the one who left you; an encounter with her, particularly if she turns away in reply to your greeting and is still remarkably pretty, will count for three-quarters of an hour's sleep." Here the Captain's face darkened a little. I could feel that the interview was approaching its close.

"Thank you, Captain," I said. "Goodbye."

"Goodbye," said the Captain, and added: "But don't make the mistake of thinking, my boy, that in cases of extreme emergency regular sleep in bed won't rest you, body and soul. And this even though I have seldom made use of it. There are people who maintain that it's a perfectly good way to rest too. So far as I can tell (because as I say I have done it only a few times myself), an hour's sleep in bed is as good as two hours' sleep. So if you lie down and sleep for an hour, it means as much as when an ordinary person sleeps two hours."

After a moment's reflection he added, "But I can't recommend that."

Chapter XIV

ONE AFTERNOON I SUDDENLY HEARD REVOLVER shots. I was living on the second floor, the Captain on the third. That was where the explosions came from. I pushed the bell, and ran into the corridor.

The revolver went on banging away on the third floor. For a moment we thought the Captain had committed suicide. But as we rushed out we were reassured, for the revolver did not stop. After six shots came a pause, then six more shots. The thing that we had begun to suspect on the way was actually happening: when we came into his room, the Captain was standing in a corner, shooting at a target in the diagonally opposite corner. He laughed at us loudly—me, the Doctor, and the chambermaid —as we stood stupid and speechless in the sour gunpowder smoke, while a little bell in the next room jingled desperately, like an invisible baby lamb hopping around on an invisible hill; Baron Kalotay, startled by the shooting, was ringing the bell at his wrist.

"I shall have to request you," said the Doctor, by this time completely embittered with his unsuccessful chase after capital, "to leave my establishment." So saying he went out, slamming the door.

The chambermaid also left. I was the only one who stayed. "What do you do such things for?" I asked, more regretfully than reproachfully, for I could feel that he was very much soured.

"Look here," he said, showing me the target he was shooting at.

It was a large group photograph, in which a whole club could be seen drawn up in four or five rows. The bottom row was seated, with the president in the middle. They all wore black cutaways, and the four members seated at the bottom left had already had their heads shot out. If we had not come rushing up, he would have gone on to shoot all the rest of the club.

"This is the best way of getting target practice in your room," he explained; "I mean a group photograph. Nothing but little targets, and all human heads, besides. It's a little more exciting. I learned this way of practicing in Paris, from a young Montenegrin, a relative of old Nikita, the Prince of Montenegro. This lad had bought up all kinds of old group pictures—clubs, schools, weddings—from the suburban photographers, just to practice with a revolver in his room. And he showed me that it's not all the same to your hand whether it's aiming at a target or at a human head. Heads are more difficult."

There was a knock. The young chef of the restaurant entered, garbed in white, with the invariable tall white cap on his head.

"Sit down, my friend," said the Captain to him. "For tonight I am going to give you a very interesting assignment. We shall get to your affair in a moment—I just want to explain this to my friend. I'm in a bad humor today; I'm getting target practice."

He got a few similar pictures out of the cupboard. There were some uninjured ones among the figures. He had done his most thorough work on a picture in which the whole Volunteer Fire Brigade of the Third Ward had been shot down. The poor firemen stood there in full-dress uniform, with a hole in place of their heads, and a helmet over the hole.

He slapped another picture violently with his hand. "Do you see that?" he said, pointing.

Under the picture it said: "St. Stephen's High School, Budapest. Eighth class, 1889." The whole class had been shot through the head; only the teacher, sitting in the middle of the bottom row, had been pierced by some sharp object. The center of the picture, around the teacher, had been torn to bits by countless shots.

"You know," he said, "it was perfectly awful. I've had this in my cupboard for years. Shooting at that picture, I saw the Devil."

I looked at him blankly. The chef laughed.

"Don't laugh," he said to the chef. "After all, you're an intelligent person. Only stupid peasants laugh at things like that. I tell you, I saw the Devil. He was sitting in this spot here, where it's torn, in the middle of the picture . . ." He pointed to the torn hole in the picture, corresponding to the teacher's seat.

"I simply bought this picture from the photographer, like all the rest. Pale, sedate little schoolboys, the eighth grade, just before graduation. So I started shooting them neatly in turn. I started up here, at the left, standing on the bench. I got along splendidly, right through the class. You see, I scarcely missed two out of thirty. I skipped the teacher, and left him to the end. When all the pupils were shot, I loaded my pistol again, and happened to look at the old teacher.

"The blood froze in my veins. The teacher, who had been sitting there with a blank expression, suddenly wore a different look now that the whole class had fallen around him. He looked at me defiantly but raptly, moving his lips a little."

The chef laughed again.

"Don't laugh," he said, a little irritated by now. "It's true if I say so. The teacher was begging for death. As if to say: 'Now that all my pupils have fallen, I don't want to go on living either.' I was horrified; and then his tiny face changed again. He said: 'Come on, shoot, kill me—I don't want to go on living without my pupils!' He looked at me imploringly, as if waiting for deliverance. I was touched to think that a teacher could love his pupils so. I was a little ashamed of having caused him such pain, and I could feel that there was no other recourse: the teacher must be shot so that he should not suffer any more. I took a good aim, and fired, and missed.

"I looked at him; his face was not anguished now, but cold and rigid. I tried again, and again the bullet missed.

"A touch of derision appeared in the tiny eyes of that cold face. 'Well,' I said, 'are you making fun of me?' I must confess that I went up closer to make sure of hitting him. I fired and missed.

"The derision spread from his eyes all over his face. I was furious. I fired at least three times; I didn't hit him.

"By now he was grinning quite unmistakably, his tiny eyes gleaming like sparks. And, my dear fellow, I fired ten times, twenty times—all for nothing. He kept grinning and grinning more and more, getting uglier and uglier, more and more terrible; you can believe me when I say I was horrified, for I could feel that I had met the Devil. So that was why the scoundrel had begged so pitifully for death, simply so that he could torment me now.

"A man can never tell in what form he will see the Devil. But at some time in his life everyone does see him. I saw him then. I fired away all the cartridges I had. Finally I pierced him with my sword, as you can see. I felt wretched, and was quite exhausted. My head ached madly. And I can still remember that the gunpowder had a much worse and more sulphurous smell than usual. It's all right for you to look at the picture now; the Devil isn't in it any more. When I pierced him, he laughed out loud, and leaped back to Hell."

The chef was listening with a grave, dismayed look.

"Now you may laugh, Spaniard!" said the captain triumphantly. "Don't feel like it any more, eh?"

The chef was known as the "Spaniard" because he had come home from Madrid to Hungary; in Madrid he had been a scullion at the Spanish royal court. And he was here now because the Captain had ordered a supper for that evening. He too had heard of the dinner that Mr. Gluck, the most scholarly Hungarian culinary artist, had recently arranged.

Mr. Gluck, who was a rich man and wrote gastronomic books, gave a reconstruction of the *Banquet of Trimalchio* in the basement restaurant of his hotel for a party consisting of male and female artists and medical authorities. With a translation of the Roman classical author Petronius' description in his hand, he decorated the dining room in Roman style, got sawdust dyed red in ancient Roman fashion to sprinkle on the floor, and then he himself went to work and produced the Roman dishes with historical accuracy, just as Petronius had described them. There was no need to imitate the wines; the fiery Italian wines of today are the same as they were in Trimalchio's time. Only there are different dates on the bottles.

The banquet was a great success. Everyone was ill. But the medical authorities cured the artists, and the artists lugged the medical authorities home. It had been a celebrated event in Budapest.

"Well," said the Captain, "we can do that sort of thing too, Spaniard. Only we aren't going to eat a Roman banquet, but a Spanish one, since you learned the higher art of cookery in the King of Spain's kitchen. I am eager to know what His Majesty Alphonso XIII is in the habit of eating. There will be four of us, and I want exactly the same supper that the Spanish king used to eat when he wanted a good meal. Absolutely the same, now!"

The chef took out a book.

"Go on, out with you!" the captain barked at him. "We shall be there on the dot of nine, and eat in the big kitchen."

The chef departed.

Chapter XV

"HAVE A SEAT," SAID THE CAPTAIN. "THIS GIRL Mercedes is ruining me. A veritable beast!"

I sat there and said nothing.

"It's enough to drive you mad! She was an ugly little thing, and now she's beginning to be pretty. When I first met her she was in rags, and now she's as fashionable as a second-rate Paris tart. When I began taking her to supper, she was stupid. Now she's as clever as the Rabbi of Ungvar. She talks loftily to me. She laughs at me for no reason. She doesn't answer my serious questions. Her nails used to be black; now she has hands like lilies. She used to be gentle and modest; now she's bold. She'll be the ruination of me."

"Why don't you get rid of her?" I asked. "You should put her away, cruelly."

"I can't be cruel to women. I'm incapable of it. I envy those who can do it. Did you know old Ferdi Gaal? He could be cruel to a woman, and to his own wife, at that. Get out your pencil and notebook. Old Ferdi Gaal was desperately in love with his wife, who was much younger than he, and deceived him all his life. He knew it, but had no strength to give up the woman. In fact to make his wife stay with him he turned over his will to her, bequeathing her his whole fortune, and gave her his word of honor that he would not change his will as long as she lived with him. He was very rich and very sick. They had no children.

"His wife stayed with him, and went on deceiving him. On his deathbed old Ferdi Gaal had his lawyer bring all his cash and all his securities from the bank, tore it all up into a thousand pieces before his wife's eyes, had himself carried over to the fireplace, and threw the scraps into the fire. The next day he died. You can put away your notebook. That was all. You young scoundrel, I can see by your face how well you like a man like that."

"Yes!" I said with enthusiasm.

He sighed deeply. "I'm not that sort of fellow, unfortunately. I'm the very opposite. This beast of mine will be the ruination of me."

I told him this was unlikely, if he could speak thus coldly and critically of her. I said she excited and disturbed him, but it didn't go deep. When I told him that, he listened most attentively. I could see that he was expecting hope, help, consolation from me, and while I was explaining to him that he did not seriously love the girl, I could see from his manner that it was very serious indeed. You had to know him; suffer passively he could not. Actions kept running through his head. What was he to do? Shoot the girl, or himself? But while I was talking, gradually taking another tone under the influence of this observation I had made, he put aside his hard, imperious mask, and listened to me again as I have very seldom seen him do—like a little child to a storyteller. For this reason I completely lost my conviction as I talked, and in the end I was uttering stale generalities, including ones I had heard or read. I discovered that he loved this girl Mercedes to distraction.

"Of course you think," he said, forcing his voice to be hard, "that I must have a terrifically intimate relationship with the girl."

The words escaped me: "Not even that?"

These words from the heart crushed him inwardly, but externally he kept his poise. "I didn't force it," he said. "Occasionally I did kiss her, but once she wiped her mouth afterwards. I can't see what's disgusting about me!"

He looked fiercely at his cigarette. Indeed there was nothing disgusting about him, not even seen through a woman's eyes—unless you made up your mind to begin with that you didn't care for him. For that is something about which nothing can be done. He was a hard, red-scrubbed, close-shaven, clean-cut man. All broad muscle and bone, strength, imagination, gaiety, dash and grace, despite his short stature. Only perhaps his legs were a bit short. I have often noticed since that women do not like this. Still it could not be the decisive reason. I am more inclined to believe that the lady disliked the Captain complete, as he was. That too has been known to happen, and it is far worse than short legs.

I was surprised at his having no affair with the little black-haired beast, but I believed him. If a person has good ears, it is hard to lie to him about that or its opposite. And if in addition the person has good eyes to watch the accused as he makes his confession, it is impossible to lie. I would not have gone through fire and water for the brunette; but that she had not given herself to the Captain was certain.

"I did something abominable," said the Captain suddenly, in the midst of my brooding. "I took dinner with her and this Oskar. With this secretary or booking agent or whatever he is, the fellow she's always with. I bought them a dinner with champagne, like any old fool. That Oskar fellow was so hungry that I was simply amazed at the way he ate. He looks like a caterpillar, and smokes so many cheap, bad cigarettes that his fingers and the corners of his mouth are stained yellow. He's an ugly, sickly fellow. And that pretty girl . . . I simply can't understand it." Smiling sourly, he shook his head.

"And that's a mere nothing," he went on. "I did something still more abominable. After dinner we took Mercedes home, and then I went to a café with Mr. Oskar. We kept on drinking until morning, and I pumped him. It's amazing, but he hasn't had any affair with her either. I don't know whom that beast *is* having an affair with. Mr. Oskar says she probably has some old, mysterious gentleman. Mr. Oskar was not lying to me. After his third drink he was completely boiled, and his tears poured like a cloudburst. I was positively ashamed, because he was even more in love than I. Of course I didn't confide in him. I pretended I simply went out sometimes with the girl for fun and to listen to her merry chatter. He poured out his heart. He really did write to Paris about Mercedes, to some Hungarian ballet master, and he wants to go there with her. He said, 'There, maybe I can get it . . .' I gave him advice. How he was to treat her thus and so. I taught him how he could make her docile; consoled him and told him he just needed a little persistence, and she would certainly be his; he mustn't give up the struggle . . . Bah! Isn't that abominable?"

"No."

"Yes it is!" he said. "You're an opportunist newspaper scribbler. And that's abominable." He smiled unexpectedly. The expression with which he had been talking about the girl—I do not know whether to call it sour or bitter—suddenly vanished. You could see that he was thinking of something he found touching. "Are you writing my biography yet?" he asked.

"Not yet. I'm taking notes."

"I asked because you've heard the story of my birth, but you still don't know anything about my early youth. Is that right?"

"Yes."

"Now that I'm talking about this girl whom I've fallen so scandalously in love with, I'm reminded of my first love. Have you got a pencil on you?"

"Always."

"Get it out. Have you got a notebook?"

"Surely."

"Take notes. Never fear, this isn't one of your ordinary sentimental stories. In fact it's very peculiar. I was twelve years old when I fell in love for the first time. With a twenty-four-year-old girl. Just twice my age. Her name was Hedvig. A beautiful, plump girl, not fat, but not thin by any means. She came to our house often, because she was my sister's best friend. My sister was twenty-four too. At that time everyone regarded me as a child. The girls never talked to me much, not even my sister. Sometimes the three of us would go out riding; you know, Father still had a small country place then, and we kept some good horses.

"So I fell in love with this Hedvig. I didn't seriously until she got married. I had loved her before better than any other girl in the world. Why? Because she smelled so nice. Don't smile. She used some sort of strong French perfume; as I have since discovered, it was probably Piver's *Trèfle Incarnat*. Whenever I caught that scent about her, the blood flew to my head. I didn't know then what it meant. Now I do know: it was love. I fell in love with her through the nose. When I was with her I could think of nothing but her scent. And when she left, I still thought about it long, long afterward. Child psychology, what? Isn't that what they call it?"

"You might call it that."

"As aforesaid, she got married. To a man by the name of Barna. Barna was much older than she. She not only hated her husband, she loathed him. At the time I could not guess why. She was unhappy, and she kept growing prettier and sweeter-scented. What was it we called that? Psychology? And you can take down also that I really fell in love with her because she married and belonged to another man. By that time I was a year older—thirteen. It's an awful feeling for a child, if you can still remember that sort of thing.

"I couldn't sleep or eat, and was incapable of preparing for my school examinations. Nothing interested me, nothing at all except Hedvig. I got up in the morning: Hedvig. I went to bed at night: Hedvig. By that time not only my nose was full of her, but my ears, my eyes, my whole life. I had her like a disease. She, of course, paid me no more attention than before.

"And you'd better take down why I hadn't the courage to stand up before her and tell her bravely: 'Hedvig, I love you.' It was because I was afraid of a slap in the face. Interesting—I wasn't afraid of what really threatened me, namely being laughed at, but of what only a grown man need fear if he says anything like that to a respectable woman— being insulted. Don't you see how love makes a man of a thirteen-year-old boy?

"Well, one day Hedvig came by train to our country house, and I could see at once that she was in some sort of trouble. She had scarcely arrived before she took my sister aside and began whispering with her. Then my mother joined them in their room, and all three of them whispered. That evening Father came home; they retired to their room again, but didn't include Father in their secret whisperings.

"It got late at night. Then Mother told Hedvig she ought not to go home to town, but should telephone her husband in Budapest that she would spend the night with us in the country. They telephoned, and her husband agreed. They made a bed for her in my sister's room.

"My sister's room was next to mine. When they went to bed, I went to my room too. There was a door between the two rooms. I trust you have already guessed that I promptly put my ear to the door, and began to eavesdrop.

"From the conversation I gathered what they had been whispering about all day. Hedvig needed money. She had stolen six hundred crowns from her husband, and was unable to get those six hundred crowns anywhere. She consulted all day with my mother and sister about how six hundred crowns were to be raised. Hedvig wept bitterly—so bitterly that my heart almost broke in the next room. She had been so desperate the afternoon before, she said, that she had tried to hang herself in the bathroom, but the rope had broken. As I told you, she had grown stouter after she married—even though she had suffered because she loathed her husband. But when she was stouter she was even prettier and sweeter-scented; I tell you I can still smell that pungent, provocative perfume now.

"Well, in a word, they couldn't get six hundred crowns anywhere. My sister didn't have as many as six. The bank wouldn't give Hedvig anything. My mother had only closely calculated money for the housekeeping. Hedvig dared not ask anything from her own parents.

"My sister gave her various pieces of advice, but she never said anything except: 'No, that's impossible.' And she absolutely had to have the money in the morning; she had to settle accounts with her husband.

"My sister advised her to tell her husband the truth about how she had taken the money. Let her husband send her to prison if he liked.

"Hedvig replied that she hated her husband so much that she would rather run away from him than confess to him that she had stolen his money. Anyone who knew the man would not have been surprised at that.

"Here there was a little mystery about the six hundred crowns. Listening at the door, I gathered from the scraps of conversation that she had given the money to another man—a poor lad whom she loved. This was a terrible complication. I trembled at the other side of the door. I was all love and anguish. Not only my heart pounded, but my stomach. It was like a heart. Hedvig lay in the next room beside my sister, sobbing.

"Well, I said to myself, this is no place for hesitation. I crept on tiptoe into my father's room—he was already sound asleep—filched his keys from the drawer, went into the next room, and took six hundred crowns out of the desk drawer where he used to keep his cash. Then I slipped the keys back into their proper place, and went to my room. I didn't undress, because I was afraid of oversleeping and not being awake in the morning when Hedvig left. To catch the first train to Budapest she had to get up at six.

"At half past six she appeared in the garden for breakfast. I was waiting for her. When we were left alone, I stood up in front of her and said: 'Hedvig.'

"She said, 'What is it, my child?'

"I said, 'Hedvig, let's not make speeches. Here are the six hundred crowns, and we'll never mention it again.'

"She looked at me. I was sure then that she had given me a lovelorn look. Child psychology. Then

she asked where I had got the money. I said it was
money I had saved up, and she should pay me back
when she could. She cried and hugged me. It pained
me terribly that now, early in the morning, right
after her bath she smelled much sweeter even than
usual.

"She asked through her tears, 'You sweet child,
how can I show you my gratitude?'

"I said, 'Kiss me on the mouth.'

"She looked at me oddly; fundamentally, you
know, I think she was probably a loose woman. She
kissed me with her ripe, warm, full lips right on
the mouth, and ran back into the house.

"Now I won't ask you to guess what I did right
afterward, because you could never guess even if
you racked your brains all night. You know what
I did? I threw up. I can't help it if my stomach re-
acted like that to the kiss my love gave me. Undoubtedly it came from the shock of too much
excitement. It happened to me the first time I tried
to smoke. Would you believe that the two greatest
passions of my life, women and smoking, began in
the same way, with my throwing up?

"The rest of the story isn't interesting. Hedvig
left. In the afternoon my father discovered the
money was missing. There was a great uproar, hunting, and searching, but I went straight to my father
and confessed that I had stolen the money. From
four in the afternoon until ten at night they were

at me to tell what I had done with the money. But I wouldn't say. I didn't get any supper. At ten in the evening I ran away to my uncle in Budapest. Have you taken it all down?"

"Yes."

"I insist on having that chapter of the book called 'Child Psychology.' Even though it's my psychology to this day. If a woman needs money, I don't care how I get it for her. Possibly a better title would be, 'Chivalric Psychology.' "

He put on his overcoat. "And now I'm going to town," he said.

"On foot?"

The question was justified, since it had been snowing incessantly for two days. The snow was so deep that not even the trolleys were running, and no sleigh would have come out to the island at any price.

"Yes sir," he said. "I'm going to fetch Mercedes. I've invited her to dinner. That's why there'll be four of us. Pharmaco and you, me and Mercedes."

"Didn't you invite the Doctor?"

"No. I can't sit at the same table with a doctor." He shivered and made a face. "At a dinner party I once sat opposite Professor Adam, the celebrated surgeon. Since that time I haven't been able to watch a doctor eat."

"What did the professor do?"

"He ate."

"Well, and so?"

"That was just it. He ate. He ate chicken. Of course you know that he's one of our best operating surgeons."

"The best."

"It made me nervous when he took his knife in his hand. The man has been operating from morning to night for thirty years. He can't help it, of course, but you can tell it from the very way he holds his knife at table. He cut up the chicken just the way he cuts up little parts of the human body!"

"You don't say!"

"Of course that's perfectly natural. Anyone cuts up meat however he's in the habit of cutting up meat. Everybody in his own way; he can't help it. But he carved the chicken at the joints, with careful precision and yet with the most lightning-like accuracy. Those short, steady, expert incisions as he cut the muscles from the little bones struck me as grisly. I couldn't look away from his hands. I kept thinking that he had acquired this stupendous skill that he was so brilliantly displaying on the roast bird opposite me by the cutting up of human viscera. I could just bear watching the operation until he speared the first bite on his fork and put it into his mouth. Then I had to leave, because I felt sick. No, no doctors at table for me! Let's not even talk about it any more. Please be punctual. I'll see you at nine in the kitchen."

Chapter XVI

IT WAS ONLY THUS I DISCOVERED THAT I TOO WAS invited to the Spanish court dinner in the big restaurant kitchen. The Captain set out through the dark on his way to town. I went back to my room, lay down on the couch to think, and fell asleep at once. I dreamed I was in Rome. Memories of a recent trip to Italy came to my mind, and I heard the tumultuous bells in Rome. They woke me up. It was nine o'clock, and pitch black. The bells went on ringing, wilder and more piercing than in my dream. Going to my window, I looked down to the door of the hotel. A sleigh stood outside with four horses. On the back of the first were two unheard-of, tremendously large and shiny instruments, ringing, jingling, tinkling, and rattling. These brilliantly nickel-plated lyre-shaped sets of bells glittered in the light of the archway; among the bells, gongs, chimes, hung long red and white horsetails. The horses nervously shook the superimposed orchestra on their backs, and made as much noise as if the whole Russian Imperial Court had arrived at the hotel in a hundred sleighs.

The Captain, with great gallantry, was just helping Mercedes out of the sleigh. She leaped down gracefully from the high sleigh, and laughed loudly. Going out into the hallway, I looked down into the lobby, and saw them go through the ground-floor corridor into the big kitchen.

Nothing extraordinary happened at supper. The so-called atmosphere was interesting. It was a monstrous kitchen, intended for two thousand holiday-makers, and it was poorly lit by a few lamps that left the corners half dark; there was a fabulous giant stove.

In the very center of the enormous kitchen was the little table for four at which we sat. The chef, clad in snow white, with his cap, brought on the favored dishes of the King of Spain, one after another. . . .

His Majesty Alphonso XIII, dear reader, begins with a heavily over-salted vegetable soup. Then he eats lobsters "a l'Américaine." Very small, and not quite fresh, with sauce so sharp that your eyes water. Then he has rather burned *tournedos* beneath which is bread toasted in butter, with a piece of goose liver lying glumly on top, like Madame Récamier on the couch that bears her name. His Majesty is then served with a large dish of vegetables in whose midst is a big, underdone, inedibly raw cauliflower, around which, like chicks around a hen, are little bright-colored heaps of carrots, peas, mushrooms, beans, and spinach. But even this is not enough for the luxury-loving Spanish monarch. He has a blazing rum-cake, burning with an open flame, then cheese, which no doubt he does not touch either, and then fruit in a tall dish. Finally he washes his hands in a little brass bowl, soap being replaced by a slice of lemon. If I had not known I was a guest of the King of Spain, I would have thought this was the ordinary annual banquet of our press association, except that there, instead of lobster, they usually have cold sturgeon, also not quite fresh, with tartar sauce. That is apparently the only difference between a Spanish court banquet and a Hungarian press-club dinner.

The culinary success of the Spanish chef, mediocre to begin with, was rather spoiled by a little incident. The Captain found two flies in the vegetable soup—two little winter flies, presumably born too soon in the warmth of the kitchen. He put down his spoon.

"Come here, Spaniard," said the Captain softly, in a warm voice. "It was really sweet of you to try and guess my tastes; but what leads you to suppose that I like my soup with just two flies? In future, let me beg you to serve the soup plain, without flies, and put the flies in a separate side dish. Then I can put as many as I want in my soup."

I have never seen a man with a dagger wound in the heart, but whenever I try to imagine one I make him look like the chef at that moment.

After supper Pharmaco sang his own songs, and

did a few nightingale imitations. Meanwhile the King of Spain had five kinds of liqueur.

This was the first time I had ever seen the Captain with Mercedes. And indeed the relationship between them was pitiful. She treated him outrageously, yet without using a single improper or offensive word. When we sat down at table, I didn't find the girl attractive at all. But after dinner, when she had grown warm with food and liqueur, her face had the laughing charm of a sorceress. Her eyes ran over us like lizards, until we could almost feel something tickling. She laughed often and senselessly, which made me nervous. She also played Queen of Spain a trifle. But whenever she laughed it was always at the Captain, and even her Spanish pride was directed solely at him. We talked about getting fat, and about various reducing diets.

The Captain said there were only two sure methods of reducing—unrequited love and financial worries.

Thereupon the girl said in shrill tones, "Just come to me, and I can get you both this very evening."

The Captain smiled a sour smile, and tried to stroke her cheek tenderly. She tossed her head with playful arrogance, imitating the pose of a queen, and slapped the Captain's hand in mock indignation.

"How dare you, sir!"

But the blow, whether by chance or from the nature of the lady, had the loud slap of an affront, and

I could not help feeling that I ought to blush for the Captain.

Suddenly there was a silence. No one said anything. The deep stillness was broken by the sound of the bells as the horses shook their heads outside the building. At this Pharmaco, with the most excellent intentions, as if to emphasize the generosity of the Captain in the girl's eyes, said, "Those musical harnesses are wonderful. They must have cost like the devil."

Mercedes said spitefully, "I don't like a man who wants to buy love for money."

We could feel that this piece of impudence was aimed at the Captain. I would have liked to change the subject, but I did not succeed. The Captain, reddening, said, "No, I never bought love for money."

Pharmaco was tactless. "Why, that's nothing shameful," he said. "Even the most famous lady-killers have not been above it if a woman took their fancy and there was no other way of making a quick conquest. In Paris, for example—"

The Captain interrupted him. "Paris is the very place where buying love for money is least to be recommended. No, thank you! One of your nocturnal acquaintances on the boulevard, outside a café, and then a visit to the lady—why, you may get murdered."

"I've heard of such cases," said the girl.

The Captain pulled his chair closer to the table. His eyes lit up, like those of someone recalling an exciting memory.

"I used to have an acquaintance in Paris," he said, "a German baron. Baron Bix. He once had a most unpleasant experience. He spoke to a pretty girl who was promenading on the Boulevard des Italiens after midnight. They went into a bar, and drank strong liqueurs. The Baron had no particular intentions toward the girl. But they drank a good deal, the girl invited him most urgently, he was very drunk, and so he accepted. The girl took the Baron to her apartment, in a dirty old building on the Rue Vintimille."

Mercedes laughed.

"What are you laughing at?" asked the Captain, irritated.

Mercedes answered, still laughing, "Weren't *you* your baron friend?"

The Captain shook his head. "Didn't you hear me say his name was Baron Bix and he was an acquaintance of mine?"

The girl went on laughing offensively. "You were too the baron, only now you're ashamed to admit that you bought a streetwalker for money."

"Nonsense!" I barked at the girl. I turned to the Captain. "Please go on."

He continued, "They went up to the fifth floor, in a dirty old building, as I said, and the girl took the Baron into a little two-room apartment. The Baron, reeling with all the drinks he had had, tossed off his clothes on the floor and flung himself full length on the bed.

"He stretched out, and tried to sleep. He lay for a long time with eyes closed, unable to doze off. Lying stretched out there, he happened to open his eyes, and glanced into the big mirror on the door of a cabinet. His dinner jacket was on the floor beside the bed. He saw the coat in the mirror.

"Suddenly he noticed that the dinner jacket was moving. He said nothing, because he thought he was so drunk he must be seeing things. But he kept a sharp watch. Again the dinner jacket moved on the carpet. By then he had caught sight in the mirror of a human hand reaching out slowly from under the bed and slowly, very slowly pulling the dinner jacket in. The Baron kept his pocketbook, full of money, in the dinner jacket. •

"He must have been terribly startled, because he still did not dare to utter a sound. The dinner jacket moved with ghostly deliberation toward the bed. Then the Baron, staring with bated breath in the mirror, also saw the head of the man belonging to the hand under the bed. All at once the man under the bed also looked in the mirror, and saw that the Baron, lying on top, was watching him silently. The eyes of the two met in the mirror and looked wildly at each other. My heartbeat stopped. . . ."

Mercedes interrupted with a screech. "Aha! You gave yourself away that time!" She screeched triumphantly on, "You gave yourself away! You said 'My heartbeat stopped.' In the first person. So you *were* the Baron, after all!"

The Captain turned pale with fury. The girl reveled in her success, shrieking, mocking, laughing like a little witch. The Captain sat mute, and his lips trembled with rage and shame. His eyes lit up.

"I wasn't the Baron," he said quietly when the girl finally fell silent. "I give you my word of honor that I was not he."

The girl yelled at him, "But you said it in the first person. You said, 'My heartbeat stopped.'"

The Captain replied gently, "Yes, because *my* heartbeat stopped."

The little witch was suddenly silent in amazement.

"Yes, yes," said the Captain with a sharp quality in his voice, "well, yes, I did make a slip of the tongue. My heart skipped a beat because I was very much startled. But I wasn't the Baron, lying on the bed; I was the man under the bed reaching out for the dinner jacket. I had reason to be startled, didn't I?"

I can't help it: at that moment I was enchanted with the Captain. The Captain breathed easier, and ordered a drink in resounding tones of command. He ordered Mumm Cordon Rouge champagne and bitter English beer to be mixed in one vessel. He said he had learned about this in America, where this mixture was known as Black Velvet.

"Just for the sake of variety," he said.

Mercedes, however, kept looking at the clock. "I've got a rehearsal tomorrow morning," she said. And then, "Come on, let's go. Those poor horses are freezing to death outside."

The Captain begged her for another half-hour, again and again, so awkwardly that I could not help being ashamed for him once more. Finally she did not even answer him at all, but reached silently for her fur coat.

The carillon that the horses outside kept jingling now and then during supper was the show piece of a Hungarian firm, and an exact copy of the one this firm had made for the court of the Russian Czar and exhibited at the Paris World's Fair. As late as that afternoon the Captain had had no idea of buying it. When he was going to call for the girl in his sleigh, for which two cabs had had to give up their four horses, he stopped outside the celebrated saddlery shop, and went in to buy the usual simple sleigh bells. There, in the showcase, he saw the show piece, the aforesaid church carillon for the Czar's sleigh horses. He bought the two instruments for a fantastic price, and gave them that same day to the two cabmen. They are long since back in the old showcase at the saddler's. The cabmen sold them at half price to the owner of the shop. I don't believe anyone will ever buy them again.

At dinner I sat opposite Mercedes. When the liqueur came around, she touched my foot with hers. I looked at her suspiciously, thinking that it was an accident. She returned my glance with a smile, and made an ironical face. She laughed loudly, and when the Captain asked her why, she said, "Later, when we're alone." I am sure—for that was her way —that driving home she told the Captain: "That long-haired boy was playing footie at dinner." In those days I cherished a sort of primeval male hatred for such women.

The meal came to an end in a forced, unpleasant atmosphere, and rather early. Mercedes was swathed in furs, and the captain sat down beside her in the sleigh. The snow had stopped; it was a crackling, Christmaslike, lovely, winter night. The black sky was full of tiny, shivering, bright stars. When the four horses threw their weight into it, the Imperial Russian Horse Orchestra on their backs sent out such a sound that I thought the whole sleeping city would awake. Then they charged off like the wind between the rows of trees, with their thick, white, snowy leaves. The jingle, growing fainter, sounded from afar long, long after—so long that I can still hear it now as I write.

We strolled leisurely through the new snow. I

was accompanying Pharmaco home to the little house.

Suddenly he stopped in his tracks, and said, "I'm going to tell you something, but you must never repeat it on your word of honor. I just want you to see what women are like. That girl stepped on my foot under the table at dinner."

I was profoundly ashamed, on behalf of the Captain. "Impossible," I said loudly, but quite without conviction.

"I swear to you," said Pharmaco, "I give you my word, she several times trod meaningly on the tip of my shoe, and looked at me each time with a smile."

I was annoyed at Pharmaco for his indiscreet boasting. I said to him rather roughly, "And what did you do?"

"Afterward I stepped on the toe of one of her shoes, and at the same time I too smiled meaningly at her. And she looked at me savagely, and said, 'Look out for my shoes.' A little later, I asked her in a whisper: 'Aren't you playing a rather dangerous game?' She made no answer to that, but simply laughed loudly and ironically."

"Well, that just goes to show," I said, "that you overestimate this whole under-the-table business tremendously. You're a conceited blockhead."

Later I learned something that explains much, though not all, of the girl's character and behavior.

She was hard of hearing. Naturally she concealed the fact. This was why she often maintained a cold, haughty silence, because she failed to hear what people said to her, and that was why she sometimes did not answer questions when failure to reply seemed presumption and arrogance. Her infuriating, senseless mirth was because she did not always hear what people said, and she thought a pretty girl's laughter was a good answer to anything.

After I had walked Pharmaco home, I strolled back to the hotel, enjoying the clear stillness of the winter night after all the English cigarette smoke, French liqueur, Spanish food odor, and Hungarian uproar. Near the hotel I saw two men walking to and fro. I knew every soul on the island by then; even from afar I recognized the two nocturnal strollers as newcomers. Turning off toward them, I discovered that they were certainly complete strangers to any of us. They were quite well-dressed, tall, strong men. Who could they be? How did they get out here on the island in this Siberian night? I rang at the front door; the doorman came down.

"Who are those people?" I asked in an undertone.

He made no reply, but signed to me with his eyes that he would shut the door first, and then talk. He shut and locked it.

"I didn't tell you," he said, "because across this snow the slightest sound could be heard over there.

While you gentlemen were eating in the big kitchen, those two came in. They sat with me in there for an hour. They inquired for the Captain. Now I ask you, what could I tell them? What do I know?"

My feet were suddenly lead. I could feel the blood draining from my face.

The doorman said in a whisper, as if still afraid his voice would carry: "Police."

Chapter XVII

I SPENT MOST OF THE NIGHT STANDING ANXIOUSLY at the window. I was waiting for the return of the Captain. Meanwhile the two tall men disappeared from my view. I grew weary, lay down, listened for some time from bed to the slightest sound, and then fell asleep.

About noon I was awakened by the doorman's appearing beside me. "The Doctor wants you to get dressed at once and come upstairs to see him."

I slipped hastily into my clothes, and ran up to the Doctor's room on the third floor. As I went I could feel that this must have some connection with the Captain, and that destiny, having taken a brief rest, was now summoning its strength to march against him.

In the Doctor's room stood an alarmingly large

electrical machine, which sometimes crackled softly, and of which I had once declared that it whispered to every newcomer, "I haven't been paid for!" Now the machine was silent. Below it in a chair sat a woman with tear-stained eyes, dressed rather shabbily, but in a so-called English suit. There was one white strand in her brown hair. She made the impression of a distinguished language mistress or the housekeeper of an aristocratic family. There was a hint of a mustache on her upper lip. The Doctor introduced me to her, mentioning my name. The lady spoke not a word.

"Sit down," the Doctor said to me severely, in the tone he usually used when telling a patient to undress, please.

The woman took out her handkerchief, and began to weep silently.

"You are the only person," the Doctor said to me, "whom this unfortunate man will pay any attention to. The apothecary is a dunce. There's no need to tell *him* anything. But you've got to speak to him."

Unfortunate man? This meant something bad. I looked at the woman, who was studying me through her tears behind a handkerchief, trying to see what kind of person it would be whom this wild man would allegedly listen to.

The Doctor turned to the woman. "Please tell him."

The woman blew her nose. (It is remarkable that this action has never been accepted among the tragic gestures, although it plays a much larger part in the vital moments of life than the clutching at heart or head so beloved of actors.)

"This gentleman," she said, "may have heard that there are detectives here on the island."

"Yesterday evening . . ."

"They're still here," said the lady. "They're watching him. A charge has been laid against him. In Buda there lives a Cabinet Councilor's widow, an old baroness. She has a thirty-year-old daughter, a beautiful girl, though already rather withered; just imagine, she never wanted to marry, and now she has fallen madly in love with him. He has betrothed himself to her, and has been her fiancé for six months. The girl's mother, the Baroness, admiring him, gave him various sums, not much, but still a substantial amount altogether, and he kept putting off the wedding, and kept getting more small sums, and then came the crash. The family learned that he was spending it on a wretched little student at a theatrical school, a certain Mercedes, and drinking champagne with her, because he was madly in love with this Mercedes. The family had him spied on, and brought a complaint to the police, for matrimonial fraud."

The lady sobbed. I discovered that I was really fond of the poor Captain, just as he was, with the awful life he led. But I had the bitter feeling that I should be unable to help him.

"Are you related to him?" I asked the lady. She had a very slight resemblance to him; I took her for his sister.

"Yes," she said, weeping. "I am his wife."

I looked at the Doctor. He got up from his desk, and began walking to and fro very fast. This was a surprise indeed. It had never occurred to me to dream that the Captain could be married.

"I have been for eight years," she sobbed into her little handkerchief. "He can't complain of me, because when I learned that these people had reported him, I immediately offered to get a divorce so that he could marry this old maid, because otherwise he's sure to be locked up. That wouldn't hurt me—it would hurt me much more if he went to prison. 'You know,' I told him, 'that I shall love you as long as I live, to the grave. Accept this divorce from me, and save yourself!' But he won't listen to any such thing; he's so self-willed that it will be the end of him. He wouldn't do that to me, he said, he wouldn't get a divorce from me for any reasons of self-interest. I told him again, I shouted at him, that he ought to save himself; he won't listen. He said he wouldn't get a divorce from me, because he said he loved nobody but me in the whole world. That he'd never loved anyone else, and I was his wife before God, and so on. The poor, dear idiot . . ."

She was weeping bitterly once more. "His heart . . . What a heart . . . Sheer goodness . . ." She blew her nose again. Something like a smile gleamed through her tears. "I once paid a bill—a good-sized one—it took all the money I had saved. Do you know what he did? It was this girl's birthday, and he sent her roses. He sent a hundred every hour. The florist's boy rang for the first time at nine o'clock in the morning, and gave her a hundred red roses. Until nine that evening the man rang punctually every hour, bringing a hundred roses each time. Thirteen hundred roses in one day. To this moment he doesn't know I paid the bill. He thinks he still owes the florist for it. And he didn't send those roses to the girl because he loved her, but out of gratitude because she loved him so much. Out of goodness."

My head reeled—what a situation! And yesterday's dinner! The Spanish menu! The chimes, the four horses, the girl Mercedes. That serene, heavenly calm! Not for so much as a moment did I guess that he had any such worries. To this day I have never been quite able to understand it.

"And then," the woman went on, "one day the old Baroness came to see me. We have a very nice four-room apartment in the Nagyfuvaros-utca, only he doesn't live there. Somehow the Baroness found this out, and, as I say, she came to see me. It was then that I learned he was a fiancé. That

he was in love with this theatrical student I had
known for a long time. But the other was new to
me, although, believe me, I have gone through a
good deal with him."

(This, I must say, I could not help believing.)

"The Baroness talked very severely to me, as
though I were somehow mixed up in the matter.
But your baronesses can't handle me. I saw immediately what was what, and denied that I was his
wife. 'Yes, I've been living with him for years, but
we aren't married.' The Baroness flew into a fury,
and didn't even say goodbye when she left. I can
well understand one of these grand old ladies when
something like that happens to her. And I must say
the situation is very difficult, because this girl simply worships my husband beyond anything I ever
heard of. For ten years she has been getting pro-
posals from the best people, but she wouldn't
marry. And when this misfortune came along, she
told her mother she didn't care even if my husband
was married, she would go with him anyhow. She
said she would kill herself for him. And believe me,
for him one could do it."

Again she had a fit of weeping. "And you have
to, too," she added.

Then she explained that she had lied to the Baroness in vain. The family's lawyer had looked into
the matter and discovered that he was her lawful

husband. The girl had given orders that no steps were to be taken against her fiancé. But the family forced the girl to go to Vienna, where the Baroness's younger sister, the wife of a rich coffee importer, took charge of her. From there the girl had smuggled a letter into the mail, telling the Captain's wife not to get a divorce, she didn't mind if they lived together *à trois*. By then the police had already begun keeping watch on the bogus Captain. It would still have been possible to get a divorce; a lawyer offered to arrange the matter in ten days. But he would have none of it.

The only thing that puzzled me was how he had had time for it all. Visiting at home—for his wife said that he often came to dinner with her—running after Mercedes, playing the fiancé to an aristocratic family in Buda, and on top of all this, creating the impression of a pensioned officer on the island with nothing to do but sit in the bushes with the apothecary nightingale, and carry on horsecar dances, parties with plum brandy, and Spanish court banquets with Black Velvet. I remembered his saying that everyone meets the Devil once in his life. To me (at least so far), it seems as if I had seen the Devil in his shape. Some sensory illusion would almost incline me to believe, after the fact, that when I saw him as a pillar of steam, the smoking vapor had a slight smell of sulphur. (I didn't notice it at the time, although I should have, for the water of the island mineral springs is very sulphurous.)

During this story the Doctor had kept on walking up and down. We had plenty of time for our consultation, because the Captain had never come back since he had last rushed out with the jingling sleigh into the night. This morning his wife had looked for him at Mercedes' apartment; he had not been there. He had brought the girl home at night, kissed her hand, and had then gone on with the sleigh. Could he have scented the detectives, and taken flight?

"I don't believe so," said the woman.

There were several long pauses. We waited. Each time there would be such stillness that we could hear Baron Kalotay's little bell jingling in the next room. What were those little lamblike bells to the jingling orgy of yesterday!

The Doctor (whom I strongly suspect of pondering, in his pacing, not only the present matter but his own pressing debts) suddenly halted in front of the woman, now staring fixedly after all her tears, and barked at her nervously, "Well, please have the kindness to tell me just exactly what you want of me."

"I told you that before," the woman replied shyly; "that's what I began with, Doctor. Please do give me an opinion that he's insane. Something about a grave nervous ailment. . . . After all, he isn't a normal person."

"Out of the question," said the Doctor. "I don't give false opinions."

"False?" the woman smiled bitterly.

"There's nothing in the world wrong with your husband. I have examined him more than once. This young man sitting here is a hundred times as nervous as he." He meant me. "There's nothing wrong with him. I can't put myself in a false position toward the police or in court. All I can do is cancel his hotel bill. He has been living here for months, and he has never paid me once."

"The servants—" I started to say.

"I know," said the Doctor. "He gives them more than the whole bill amounts to. I'm the only one he has thus honored; he has never paid me a penny of fees."

Here the Doctor's long-suppressed Weltschmerz burst forth. He addressed his plaintive words to me, who also owed him money. "I do charge fees for my examinations—small ones because it is a principle of mine that we nerve specialists must keep the costs of nerve treatments from increasing the patient's nervousness. And in any case, please don't suppose that I depend on his money. There's a deeper meaning to it. The doctor needs his fee not only to live on, but chiefly so that his work will not seem worthless."

He yelled at me sarcastically, "You can write that down in your notebook, too!"

"Thank you," said I, blushing.

Chapter XVIII

THE TELEPHONE RANG. THE DOORMAN WAS RE- porting that the Captain had arrived. The Doctor asked him to come up at once. We spent several strange and excited minutes waiting for him. I looked down from the window, but the detectives were nowhere to be seen.

He was not quite so cheerful as usual when he came in. He went over to his wife and hugged and kissed her for a long time. He clasped her tightly as if never to let her go again. His wife embraced him fervently also, but that was nothing to the embrace—wilder than the embrace of one infatu- ated—in which he pressed to him this slender woman, not thin but worn. She was half a head taller than he, but during the embrace she sank down like a swooning maiden on the verge of dis- solution. And he kissed her not on the mouth, but wherever he could—eyes, cheeks, forehead, hair, nose, hands.

I shall never forget that unsensual embrace. Men condemned to death perhaps kiss their mothers so. He was not at all ashamed in our presence. I watched both with tense vigilance. So this honest wife was a woman after all, a neglected woman. You could see that this masculine force, fueled by pure emotion, sent a great sensual wave through her.

The embrace sharply characterized the relationship between the two: the infinite friendship of the man and the deathly love of the woman. Can there be a happier, more balanced relationship between woman and man? Now at last I am able to envy the Captain for it—and his wife too.

But he was not a captain any longer. He had on a rather ill-fitting, loudly checked civilian suit. In it I must say he looked like a somewhat unreliable unemployed waiter who had knocked around the southernmost part of America—like a ship's steward, in fact. They sometimes have the same look of cheap dash, perhaps because they have to contend not only with their trade, but with hurricanes.

"Please don't speak," he finally said to us. "I know everything, and you know everything."

"Do get a divorce," wept the woman.

"I won't get a divorce," he said casually, "I'm not going to get a divorce."

"But the police—"

"I know."

He looked at me with a smile. "Well, Mr. Biographer," he said, "this will be something to write about."

I lowered my eyes. It is more than thirty years ago now. I never dreamed then that I should be sitting in a hotel room, actually writing about his life.

"There's one solution," he said pretty calmly; "flight."

The woman heaved a blissful sigh. She smiled.

I was less sure he would succeed. I ventured a word. "The detectives . . ."

"Oh, what the hell!" he said. "Do you know where I'm going? To the island of Java. There are still opportunities there. From Java I shall send you money" (this to his wife), "and you can come to join me. A brother officer of mine is living there, an honest Jewish fellow; I hear from him all the time."

"Rado?" I asked gently. "The man with the viper?"

His eyes wandered unsteadily. I could see how gladly he would have said yes, but at this moment he too felt that he was standing quite naked before the three of us. He swallowed once, and said, "No, another one."

The two detectives, meanwhile, were keeping warm in the little stone lodge of the bridge guards at the southern tip of St. Margaret's Island, on the causeway from St. Margaret Bridge. The drifting ice was crashing in the Danube; there was no other road from the island to Java. Or at least so the detectives thought. They never dreamed anyone could be so daring as to cross the broad Danube in a skiff through those huge, wildly rushing chunks of ice. They believed they were keeping a good watch over the Captain from the stone lodge, and inconspicuously at that.

He, however, crossed an hour later in the same skiff that had recently been used to bring the fifteen quarts of *Szilvorium* for the cardplayers from the dive in old Buda; making the eastern bank, he escaped the detectives. The Spanish king's chef, who had gone with him, brought the skiff back through the drifting ice.

I do not believe there was a single person on the island, the Doctor excepted, who would not have helped him in his flight. And even the Doctor was not quite unmoved, for he recommended a companion upon his trip across the river—the apothecary. The Captain laughed aloud, and would have none of it.

It is strange what comes out in a moment of danger: he was fond of Pharmaco, but did not take him seriously. The chef, on the other hand, he did. To him he entrusted his life, for the man had traveled about Spain in his youth, and so the Captain scented a dash of adventurous blood. Not for nothing does one go from the Court of Madrid to snow-covered St. Margaret's Island, to be the chef of an empty restaurant.

From a tower room (there are three of these on

the hotel roof) we looked after him with opera glasses, his wife and I. He rowed as well as if he had never pretended to be a captain, but a ship's lieutenant. This was the moment when I learned that he had never been an officer of hussars.

I said to his wife, "Even though he's a hussar, he rows like a—" "Seaman," I started to say.

But his wife interrupted me very nervously, "Do let the poor fellow be—we may have any amount of extra trouble on that account. He was never a hussar in his life, not even a soldier. How many tears have I not shed over that hussar business!"

She smiled as she wept. "Once, just once, I laughed at one of his hussar tales," she said. "He told it to me when we had been married for two weeks. It was the story of his riding stark naked down the main street of a little provincial town in broad daylight, at noon, when he was a young lieutenant of hussars, for a bet."

"And you believed him?"

"Then, yes. There was a slight touch of probability to the thing. He said he had made a bet with another lieutenant of hussars for a case of champagne that he would ride down the main street at noon without any clothes—he would not wear anything except the shako on his head.

"He won the bet. He solved the problem by going early in the morning to the theatre, where he was well acquainted with all the actors. He undressed completely in one actor's dressing room, and the players simply painted the uniform on his naked body with the kind of tempera paints that they use for scenery. First the light blue tunic, then on top of it the heavy lacing with gold paint. Below, the scarlet breeches, then the black boots—these with real shoe polish, raised to a high shine with a brush. Then he stuck a shako on his head, went out of the stage door, mounted his horse, and rode—though at a mad gallop—through the midday sun down the main street, straight to the Turkish bath, where he washed himself off and put on his uniform, brought over there meanwhile by the actors. He gave the actors the case of champagne he won."

She laughed a gentle, weary laugh. You could see that she still enjoyed the story—I mean the man who had told it to her. I did not tell her that this story had once actually happened, in the town of Arad; it was a true occurrence, only it happened not to her husband but to Sz. K., an officer of hussars, who was cashiered from the army for his prank.

The skiff disappeared from our view, turning in beyond the peninsula of Ujpest. She sighed and put the opera glasses on the table. Weary and broken, she sat down in an armchair. I offered her a cigarette.

"Thank you," she declined, almost coolly; "I'm not a modern woman."

We sat there silent, and I watched her attentively.

Once she had probably been beautiful and proud. I confess she moved me. I felt I had just seen something very rare—something that later, when I had more experience of women, I might have called "true love."

The woman read my thoughts. She said simply, "It's impossible to love a human being more than I love him."

What moved me was that she said this flatly, apparently quite without emotion, as if she were propounding a mathematical theorem. If only actresses could ever muster the courage to speak such a sentence in the way she had just spoken it!

I studied her exalted features and her extraordinarily sculptured hands. "Are you descended from a family of aristocrats?"

"No," she said. "But I'm descended from an old noble family—a family much older than most Hungarian aristocratic families, and accordingly much haughtier."

"I can't imagine your ever being haughty in all your life."

"Ah, but how haughty I was! My marriage has taught me to be humble. I was the haughtiest girl in all our city. Have you the faintest idea how haughty I was? May I tell you a story, too, just to describe the old Hungarian world I came out of?"

"Please do."

"I was thirteen. One day I saw our young kitchen-maid bathing in the lake. I was startled beyond words when I saw she had breasts just like mine, and I a young lady of most noble birth. I cried bitterly all night over that. Next morning I bought some gold paint, locked my door, and gilded my little breasts. I went around for weeks afterward being proud of my noble golden breasts sparkling under the lace of my chemise. Well . . . I've tried to do the same with my sufferings; but there's no gilding them."

She gave one last look out of the window, in the direction where the skiff had disappeared with her husband. Then she said goodbye to me, and left. She went away without a penny, for at the last moment she had stuffed what little change she had had into the Captain's pocket. (I can't help it, I shall never call him anything else. Law is law, but to me he, poor fellow, will always be a captain for the rest of our brief span.) I had no money. I dared not ask any of the Doctor for the woman; he had lost money enough through the Captain. For a moment I considered getting something from Baron Kalotay for the poor woman; but I did not want to give away the secret. It is a fact that on that day all of us on the island were abettors and accomplices. But aside from all this, the chief secret I guarded was my firm conviction that the Captain would not flee alone, but would do anything to take the girl Mercedes with him. At the very moment when he uttered the word "flight," I could feel that he was thinking of the travel-loving girl, and that he was now splendidly combining the two agonizing necessities of his life in one mad solution—possessing the pretty beast, and escaping prison.

Chapter XIX

WHEN THE WOMAN WAS GONE I WENT BACK TO my room and dropped on the bed to catch a little sleep. But the few moments during which a lofty ethical phenomenon, the "perfect wife," appeared to me before the background of our rather loose-living society disturbed me so that I could not get to sleep. I tried to apply severe scrutiny to the woman's behavior toward her husband. But she withstood the most searching criticism.

To me it is always disturbing to discover something perfect in a human being. As I lay there brooding, smoking one cigarette after another, I continued to develop my theory of "perfect," or, in popular terms, "too beautiful," things. My theory was—and still is—that such "too beautiful" things are not pleasing to God.

Again and again I thought of my two-room apartment in town. An enviable feature of the apartment was what first led me to fear "too beautiful" things. For the apartment was one hundred percent fireproof. It was on the second floor, with windows and balcony giving on a quiet, narrow street, and opposite my balcony was the firehouse of the Second Ward. Three tremendous arched doors, within which stood three red automobile monsters covered with ladders, hose, nickel and brass trimmings—all the innovations of modern fire fighting. I had been living there winters for ten years, and I practically knew each fireman personally. As I read in bed with the window open of a quiet night, I would often hear the alarms come in by telephone across the way. Then I would put down my book and go out on the balcony; by the time I was out, the three big doors would be open, the huge, fire-eyed dragons would have crawled from their caves, and my brave friends would be sitting in neat rows on the backs of the motorized monsters, shouting to me where the fire was. Then they would rush off with dreadful ringing and the howl of sirens. I would not go back to bed, but would keep on reading at my desk, waiting for them to return. There was something atavistic about it: my father had been a doctor, and whenever he had an urgent call by night, we used to sit up and wait for him to get back.

In short, these are the essential points: 1. My apartment was about a hundred feet from an up-to-date fire department; 2. I was on terms of personal friendship with the firemen; 3. My apartment was on the second floor; 4. My windows were large, and directly opposite the windows of the firehouse. That is, if (God forbid!) a fire had broken out in my apartment, we should have had the rare situation wherein the firemen would not even have had to leave their building, but could simply have put out the fire by playing the hose from their own quarters into mine. And this with even more zeal than usual, since a good friend was involved. Never since the invention of fire departments had there been an apartment better situated with respect to the firehouse. Exaggerating very slightly, I might even say I was living in the firehouse itself.

Yet even so I was more afraid than anyone that my apartment would be gutted some day. Why? Because what I have just told was *too beautiful.* When I thought of the relationship between my apartment and fire, the thing that ran through my mind was not what I have been setting down, but the following dialogue between two of my friends:

"Did you hear? F. M.'s apartment was completely burned out!"

"You don't say! How did it happen?"

"Just imagine—his apartment is across from the firehouse, he has known the firemen personally for ten years, he lives on the second floor, his great big windows are directly opposite the fire-hose, and *still, still* his apartment burned!"

I could never shake off the notion that this sentence was so natural, its form so oft heard, so healthy and human, the breath of life and experience so apparent in it, that this one was closest to truth, not the sentence above in which I have listed my safeguards.

How often have I heard someone say, "And just imagine, that woman, that respectable mother of a family with four children, and not even pretty, who has hardly stirred out of the house in twenty years, who has sacrificed herself to her husband and children, never worn a smart dress, never gone to the theatre or out in society, never danced, who has attended church regularly—that model of decency and morality, just imagine, *that* woman ran away yesterday with a taxi driver, and took all her husband's securities with her!"

Or: "And just imagine, that cashier, the pride of the firm for forty years, with never a single mistake in his accounts for forty years, never a penny missing in forty years, whom I would have trusted blindly with all I own—why, *that's* the man who absconded last night after embezzling hundreds of thousands!"

And the everlasting, invariable story of the man who was never sick in his life, and yet just now, all of a sudden, died.

No, I hate perfect things. They are upsetting, frightening. They make me uneasy.

A wise Hungarian cardinal once said that St.

Paul is the greatest of saints because there was a sin in his life; early in his career he hated Jesus, and pursued His disciples with the sword.

. . . Such were the thoughts of a skeptical young man who believed he was encountering a perfect human being for the first time in his life.

Chapter XX

I WAS LIKE A PRISONER ON THE ISLAND ALL DAY, FOR owing to the tremendous masses of snow the fares of the sleighs that could be ordered out by telephone varied from fifty to sixty crowns. In those days I used to get sixteen crowns for a short story, and I could not sell more than five a month if I tried hard. Plays in those days fetched very little money even when the managers paid up, which was not always the case. I was able to eat on credit in the Royal Spanish kitchen; I could go on owing the hotel bill —that was not bad.

In the afternoon I ventured as far as the bridge. The two detectives, smoking their pipes, were sitting in the one-room stone lodge with the bridge guards, watching the three attendants play cards with awful gravity, just for the sake of the game, not for money. It was about five hours before that the Captain had rowed away, but I felt as serene as if he had already reached Java.

As I was undressing that evening, there was a faint knock at my door. I recognized the doorman by his knock. He came in, and said, with a face of horror, "Could you please come?"

I rushed after him in shirtsleeves; he had already gone ahead down to the ground floor, where the hotel had a small lobby, and where to right and left, between fat pillars, there stood two sets of furniture consisting of chairs, couch, and table. On one set, upon the couch, sat the two detectives. Before them on the table sat the Captain, smoking a cigarette. Seeing me, he laughed.

"Well," he said, "I suppose you thought I was in Java by now."

I stood agape.

"By your leave, gentlemen," he said to the detectives, "a brief consultation. May I?"

One detective nodded permission. From the look of the plain-clothesman I could see that he had grown fond of the Captain.

"Thank you," the Captain said. Taking me by the arm, he led me over to the other set of furniture. He put me on the couch, and sat down beside me.

"Telegraphic style," he said. "By skiff to town. Then by tram to black beast. Not at home. Out to suburban theatre where she is playing. Not there. Double time to Oskar's. 'Where is she?' 'Don't know. Maybe with the mysterious old gentleman.' I say: 'I'm in a terrible hurry.' Was going with her

to Paris. Didn't want to go to Java. Lied to you.
Guessing game with Mr. Oskar where she could be.
Mr. Oskar suddenly smiles. 'What goes on?' I ask.
He squeezes my hand silently and says, 'Thank you.'
I ask: 'What for?' He says: 'For good advice.' I
say: 'I don't understand.' He says: 'I had her.' I say:
'What did you have?' He says: 'Mercedes, this morn-
ing. At last.' I say: 'What?' He says: 'She had a
Spanish dinner with you on the island in the evening,
and she was in fine fettle. You took her home. But
she couldn't sleep, and came to see me at the Café
Meteor, where I sit every night. We drank a great
deal of *Baraczk*, and she came home with me. She
slept at my place. Left this morning at nine.' Mr.
Oskar was radiant. That is what happened, O author
of my biography."

"All right, all right, but . . ." I pointed in alarm
at the detectives.

"Good God," he said, "at first I thought I would
flee with her. I have already told you she would be
the ruination of me. When I went reeling away
from this Oskar fellow, I didn't know what to do.
The very spittle was bitter in my mouth. The whole
idea of flight was so empty. I'm tired. Just imagine—
fleeing alone, being afraid, hiding . . . I wouldn't
have hidden. We could have lived like kings in Paris
as long as my money lasted, and then possibly something or other would have happened if that beast,
that lovely little bitch . . . It's awful to be going

to prison now, and never to have possessed her. Mr. Oskar possessed her."

"Yes, yes," I stammered, "but then? Here? What about these two?"

He shrugged. "I was like an idiot," he said, "and I went away perfectly stunned; I came here on foot. I don't think I meant to come at all. But something lured me down from the bridge. Possibly those two detectives. I knew they were running around the island somewhere, and still I came. I'm tired—I want to sleep. I didn't sleep last night. I took her home, and then sat in the Café Cairo until morning. A hundred paces from the Café Meteor, where they were sitting drinking *Baraczk*, the beast and Mr. Oskar. Mr. Oskar, who 'had' the beast. I never had her. Mr. Oskar says she has no mysterious old man, but is called for once a week for a young Archduke. He says that's why she's so proud."

He looked almost lovingly at the two detectives. "I'm tired," he said. He pretended to be yawning, but behind the yawn he choked back an irresistible, interrupted sigh.

We sat there in silence for a long time. Meanwhile I could think of nothing except the fact that when I left the lobby the detectives would immediately cut off all the buttons from the Captain's trousers with their pocketknives. This the Captain did not yet know. A sickening feeling weighed down my stomach as I imagined the humiliating moment. At that time it was a rule of the Budapest police to handcuff only the dangerous criminals, such as robbers and murderers, when they were arrested. On others an old but neat police dodge was employed. To prevent them from running away while they were being taken to headquarters, the police cut every button off their trousers, and took away their suspenders. The prisoner had to hold up his trousers with both hands to avoid losing them. Without both hands free a man cannot run. He who lets go of his trousers and tries to run will get tangled up in them, and fall. It was a painful thought that this would happen to that man of all men. When, after a long silence, he held out his hand to me and signaled to the detectives that he was ready to go, I raced upstairs three at a time like a sprinter to avoid seeing him.

Chapter XXI

THE NEXT DAY AT NOON THE DOORMAN CAME TO my room, and handed me a fat envelope. "The Captain sends this to you," he said.

"Didn't the detectives take him along?" I asked in surprise.

"They took him, yesterday evening. The moment you rushed up to your room. But before he left, it was his last wish that I should go to his room, take this yellow envelope from his drawer, and give it to you. He said I wasn't to wake you up in the morning, because you don't like it, but to wait until noon, until you woke up."

"Did they cut off his trouser buttons?"

"Yes, all of them."

The envelope was inscribed: "Important Supplementary Documents for my Biography."

"Do you think," asked the doorman sympathetically, "that he'll go to prison?"

"I'm afraid he will."

The doorman went out, sighing, and I opened the envelope. It contained pages and pages of longhand. A manuscript in the Captain's writing, with the same heading as the envelope: "Important Supplementary Documents for my Biography."

I read it, and copied it out word for word. I reproduce it here without change. It read as follows:

Please use these lines as you think best. I am no writer, so you will think my style amateurish and rather anachronistic. But I insist on having this in my biography, as a sort of background. I come from an old noble family. My ancestors were mostly adventurers and soldiers of fortune. With them I am not particularly concerned. I had just one forebear whom I think of with love, indeed with considerable emotion, and he lived in the Middle Ages on the peak of a rocky mountain, in the now ruined castle of Teplic.

By profession he was a robber baron. The people of the countryside called him the Purple Boar. He made a living by going out at dusk, armored from head to foot, charging down with his troop of horsemen into the valley that wound below the mountain, and plundering the peaceful traders who were traveling along with their loads of merchandise. He did it out of revenge, because he had premonitions that after six hundred years the descendants of these merchants would be moneylenders, and would exploit his insolvent cavalry-officer descendants. For that reason the Purple Boar stood in my eyes on an ethical foundation, and I hold his memory in higher esteem than that of any other robber baron. His story has been passing from mouth to mouth down the generations of our family for six hundred years.

The Baron had a wife whom he worshiped, and three little daughters. The first one was seven years old, the second six, the third five. One autumn day the Baron's wife died, still young. The Purple Boar became a widower, his three little daughters were orphans.

The Purple Boar surrendered to grief, in fact he became melancholy. He looted the merchants morosely, and languidly pulled off the ears of anyone who dared to resist him. It was a specialty of his, which his neighbors learned from him. At home he would often plunge his red mustache and his red nose into his five-gallon mug, and not take them out for hours.

The little girls in the next room screeched and wrangled. They were dirty and unkempt, as befits such motherless little angels; all sorts of tiny creatures fastened upon them.

At such times the Baron would come out of his mug, look mournfully around with his tiny, lidless pig eyes, and roar with agony: "It's a mother they need! It's a mother they need!" Then he would put his head back into the mug, which contained not wine but juniper brandy, a predecessor of the drink the English call gin. The Baron's bellow would die away like distant thunder in the other mountains, upon whose peaks dwelt other robber barons, robber counts, and robber knights, all of whom lived on the same twenty or thirty merchants. Now the Baron would pull off their ears, now the Count. The merchant, poor devil, would wait until his ears had grown out again, and then a count or a baron would come and pull them off again.

Every night the neighboring aristocrats would hear the anguished howling of the Baron without his mate, and they would tremble. In the valley, however, the vassals put their heads together; they it was who called the Teplic baron the Purple Boar, on account of his red hair and his big, boar-like tusk, and they beseeched God daily to give the

Baron's little daughters a good, kind mother, who would wash the dirt off them with warm water, and comb the slow, sad, tiny creatures from their golden hair.

One fine day a voluptuously built young blond widow appeared in the castle. She wanted to see the Baron.

"You can't see him now," said the major-domo, "he's in the mug."

The woman made a tremendous fuss until the major-domo went in and shouted into the mug, "There's a wench here."

A voice replied from the brandy fumes: "Pretty?"

"Yes."

At this the Baron seized his own forelock with his own hand, and pulled his head out of the mug. "Send her in," he said. The major-domo admitted the woman.

She came in, cast down her eyes, and said, "In their mother's stead I will be your daughters' mother."

The Purple Boar scrutinized the woman from head to foot, and smiled at her. "You're a fair woman," he said. "Turn around."

The woman turned around, blushing, and asked tremblingly, looking over her shoulder, "Do you like me?'

"Uh-huh," said the Baron. Trembling, the

woman whispered, "In their mother's stead I will be their mother." Clergymen rushed into the banquet hall and instantly united the Baron in matrimony with the blond woman. They were in such a hurry because everyone was afraid the temperamental Baron would marry the woman before the clergymen had time to perform the ceremony.

The blond woman went at once to comb the children's hair, and the Purple Boar pushed his head into the five-gallon mug with both hands.

Now, my young friend, you may suppose that the widowerhood of the Baron and the orphanhood of the children was at an end.

Such was not the case. Of the three girls, only the smallest came to love the plump blond woman. This littlest one was always hanging around her neck.

But the other two put their heads together obstinately, and thought up all kinds of names for their new substitute mother. They would not even talk to her. They hated her as one can hate no one but a stepmother. For that reason the Baron was happy for only a few days. Then he grew morose again, summoned an architect, and had a new two-gallon annex built on to the five-gallon mug. Once again clouds of grief hung dark over the castle of Teplic. And again the aristocrats of the neighboring peaks heard the Purple Boar bellowing out into the black of night, "It's a mother they need! A mother! A mother!"

The vassals in the flowery valleys put their heads together again, to ask God to help the Baron. The two poor little girls, meanwhile, were dirty and full of vermin; only the littlest one was clean, sweet, and happy.

Now the merchants in the valley started a movement to have a second mother go up to the Purple Boar. They cared little for the fate of the orphans, but were afraid for their own ears, because the Baron had left these undisturbed during the few days of his happiness.

And in fact the movement was a success, for one fine spring day another woman reported at the castle. She was a tall, slender, black-haired woman, into whose eyes the merchants put atropin before she went to the castle so that her pupils would widen and her gaze would be deeper, blacker, and fierier.

The major-domo said to the woman, "The baron has just gone into the new, enlarged mug."

But the woman was not to be put off. "You tell him that a mother has come for his remaining two daughters."

The major-domo knocked on the mug.

"Come in," the Baron bubbled.

"There's a mother here," reported the major-domo.

At these words the Purple Boar stuck his head out of the mug. There were gray threads in his once fiery beard, and his eyes were sad. "Bring her in," he said.

The woman came in, and did not cast down her eyes, but looked at the Baron. "You still have two daughters," she said in a resounding, metallic voice. "I will be a mother to them in their mother's stead, and instead of their stepmother too. Do you like me, Baron?"

The Baron looked so avidly at the slender, black-haired woman that the clergymen came rushing in again and married them. The merchants danced with joy in the flowery valley. For some time now they actually suffered no bodily harm, and the Baron's men merely took their goods, against a receipt. This, however, they regarded as the proper, usual, and undisturbed method of doing business: the merchants would buy silk, stuffs, colored Venetian glass beads, and gold bullion, abroad, and all this the aristocracy at home would forcibly take from them. It was remarkable that the merchants were able to live under circumstances like this, and that some of them, indeed, made great fortunes nonetheless.

But one day the inhabitants of the valley saw the architect slowly climbing the mountain toward the castle, along with his masons. "What's this, what's this?" asked the merchants, with evil forebodings.

"The Baron is having new gallons built on," replied the architect. "This time we're going to build on five more gallons at once on the mug, because only the middle child has come to love the black-haired woman. The oldest girl will have nothing to do with her, does not speak to her, and is growing dirtier day by day. All the little creatures are in her golden hair now. The Baron is very much embittered." This was what the architect said.

The merchants were in despair, and not without reason, for the very next day at twilight the Baron and his men sallied forth from the castle, took away their stuffs and gold bullion, and pulled off the ears even of those who did not resist. All night he kept bellowing, "It's a mother they need! A mother! A mother!"

The vassals looked up to heaven, where the good Lord lived, and with imploring eyes they mutely beseeched him to send aid to the Baron and the third little orphan child. Especially since two little children were happy in the castle, and only the third, the eldest, was dirty and deeply miserable.

Well, my dear young friend, as our family tradition has the story, another woman went up to the castle. A third woman. She was scarcely in the banquet hall before the clergymen came rushing in, dragged the unhappy father out of the giant mug, and promptly married this woman as well to the Baron, dripping with brandy as he was. The oldest

girl hesitated for two or three days, became reconciled, and grew fond of the new stepmother;
from then on she too was cheerful, clean, merry,
pretty, and happy.

The merchants positively swam in bliss, and
danced and sang all day and all night in the flowery
valley. One of them grew so saucy that he rented a
castle on the top of one of the mountains, and looted
his own fellow-merchants, pulling off the fresh-
grown little pink ears.

And so now that all three children had their
mothers the Purple Boar undressed every afternoon
and crawled into the mug, and only poked his head
out of the brandy once an hour for air. The mothers
brought up the three little girls.

A few months passed in general bliss in this fashion, and then the Baron shouted out of the mug,
"Now the children have their mothers, and it's
about time for me to start looking after my own
interests. Bring me a blooming maiden with tender
white skin, for it is high time that I got married
on my own account."

Whereupon there came up from the valley a
maiden with milky white-and-pink skin, who was
married to the Purple Boar halfway up, on the slope
of the mountain. The girl had straw-yellow hair,
hands as small as the flower of the jasmine, charming
calves, and such tiny feet that the shoemakers
laughed when they took her measure. She went up

to the castle, where she was dressed in silk and sprinkled with juniper brandy, the better to please the Baron.

There was no living with the merchants; they nearly jumped out of their skins with joy. The common people spoke reverently of the Purple Boar, who was now living with four women. According to legend, however, whenever anyone spoke the name of the Purple Boar thus reverently, he also spat—he and all others present. This was because the common people considered it immoral for the Baron to have three mothers and a wife, thus replacing the one woman who had borne his children. People replaced his fine name of Purple Boar with the more vulgar, ugly, indeed positively pejorative cognomen of Red Swine, and called him by it thence-forward. All this abhorrence of the Baron was due to the fact that the common people in those days could not think deeply, and therefore did not know that the Baron with his four wives was in the right.

I as a child of a later and enlightened age, as a captain, particularly as a captain of cavalry, cannot make myself ridiculous in your eyes by suddenly turning sentimental at the end of this story. I am convinced that when the Baron died he went straight to Hell, where he is boiling to this day in a huge kettle—not in oil, I trust, but in brandy. Yet I am compelled to defend the action of my great ancestor. I feel that when a mother dies she dies forever, and it happens only once in a lifetime that the same woman is loved by all the children and by the father of these children. If she dies, usually stepmothers, governesses, maidservants, nurses, doctors, and teachers, more women and still more—dark-haired, blonde, grave or jolly, fat and thin, short and tall, beautiful and more beautiful, good and yet better—make their appearance, but still they do not add up to one mother. The fact that my celebrated ancestor the Purple Boar took four women, and that these four sufficed, does not prove that the Purple Boar was a red swine, but rather leads one to conclude that the Purple Boar was extraordinarily fortunate.

My dear young friend, the merchants with the pulled-off ears and the vassals drew the conclusions consequent upon the case from the standpoint of commerce and public safety. But you as a poet will have to draw the ethical conclusion, not because you live by doing so, but because poets were put into the world for that purpose.

Chapter XXII

AS I DID EVERY YEAR, I MOVED TO THE LITTLE HOTEL, now run not by the Doctor, but by a new corporation. I had not been able to spend the whole winter on the island for financial reasons, because in the end communication with the city became quite impossible on the means at my disposal. And I was not at all happy thus—shall we say?—alone, after the Captain had been taken away and sentenced to months in prison. Only when he was gone did I discover that on the island the captain was not a mere person, but an institution.

As often as I thought of him, which was very often, I grew sad. At these times I would rack my brains wondering how the Captain would behave in prison. What thoughts occupied his mind? What would he be like when he was released? Would he have changed? Would not these months in prison make a human wreck of him?

I was somewhat reassured by a letter that he wrote to me from prison two weeks after he was sent up. He wrote from Szeged, from the Star Prison, so named not because the stars of crime were incarcerated there, but because the wings of this modern prison were built in star shape around a center. The letter of course went through the hands of the warden, and bore official numbers and rubber stamps.

The salutation was "Dear Sir." I was sorry that he had not dared to call me "Dear Friend," although he had always addressed me so.

"Get out your notebook," he wrote, "and take down the following. In this prison there are two scoundrels who owe their punishment to the invention of the airplane. One of the rogues is a mechanic, the other a professional pickpocket. Now that Blériot has flown the English Channel, many aviators are putting on exhibition flights in Europe. They, however, always display their aeronautics in big cities.

"My two fellow-prisoners, on the other hand, craved only the applause of the inhabitants of small towns and villages. They banded together. They hired an airplane, and went before the public in the provinces, in small towns and villages, always at the time of the country fairs, when many prosperous farmers, peasants, and the like were gathered even in little places.

"The exhibition consisted of the mechanic's circling in the plane over the market place, whereupon hundreds and hundreds of peasants who had never seen a flying machine before in their lives naturally stood and stared openmouthed into the air while the pickpocket stole all the money out of all the pockets of all the peasants.

"The two shared the stolen money, but not fifty-fifty; the flyer got a third, and the pickpocket two-thirds. As always in our European economic system, the thief got the larger share. Otherwise I'm in good health, and beg to remain, with very best regards, sincerely yours."

Thank God, I thought, prison has not broken the spirit of my raconteur. Thank God he has succeeded too in winning the favor of the warden, who otherwise would never have let such a letter go out of the Star Prison.

Sometimes I would sit by the fabulous great stove in the kitchen, and talk about the Captain with the Spanish chef. But I did not enjoy these conversations, for the chef took the matter very lightly. "He'll come out," he said, "and go on as he used to." He claimed to know that style of confidence man.

Pharmaco perfidiously abandoned the Captain in his heart. He said, "I wouldn't have thought it of him, though I always did know he was a common swindler."

Harsh words from a friend. I remembered that the Captain had once told me Pharmaco was a nice boy, but not a real friend. He reached this conclusion in a strange fashion. Pharmaco once attempted suicide in his little unheated room behind the apothecary shop—why, I have never known. He took a dangerously large dose of veronal, which might almost have been described as the fashion at that time among the heroes and heroines of Budapest night life.

There was a suicide wave during the first decade of the twentieth century in Budapest. Authors, actors, actresses, cardplayers, even politicians, often resorted to the revolver and veronal. (To be unkind, they were a bit careful about the direction of the revolver bullet and the quantity of veronal.)

The Doctor flushed out Pharmaco's stomach and gave him an injection of strychnine. Pharmaco slept uninterruptedly for thirty-six hours, and when he woke up he reached unhesitatingly for the cognac bottle.

As we have already seen, Pharmaco was a sentimental donkey. Before swallowing the veronal he wrote out a will on a sheet of paper, and put it in the center of his table. He was as poor as a church mouse. In his "will" he bequeathed his whole fortune —a few books, sheet music, clothes, ties, hats, shoes, his umbrella, his alarm clock, his opera hat, his roller skates, his safety razor, his watch and chain, his comb, his brush, his fountain pen, and his pocket-knife—giving one of these as a memento to each of his friends.

The Captain showed me this list while Pharmaco was sleeping his long veronal sleep. He made me read the whole list, and inquired, "Don't you see anything peculiar about the list?"

I ran through it again. "No," I said.

"I'm not on it," said the Captain, with the expression of a man suffering the bitterest disappointment of his life. "Everyone else inherited something, but I didn't. Not so much as a toothbrush."

"He forgot it in his great anguish," I said.

"That's just it," said the Captain.

Anyone who knew the Captain could not help knowing that although he would never show it, he had banished Pharmaco from his heart forever. He now proved that he had been right.

Pharmaco was not my friend, but I could not say I disliked him. He was not very bright but had a sort of childish imagination, as shown by the nightingale affair, the horsecar ball, the will. I owe it to a historian's objectivity to show him from his better side as well.

In the winter he was once invited to a studio party of young painters, which consisted of the painters' sitting from night until morning around a big table in the middle of a huge studio, toping and singing drunkenly.

Among them was a painter who could not stand liquor, so dead drunk that he scarcely knew what he was doing. He felt unwell, and began imploring the party to take him home and put him to bed.

They made no answer, but went on singing.

The weather was terrible, with rain coming down in buckets, and an icy wind. The poor painter lived miles and miles away from the warm studio.

But he implored so heartrendingly, "Take me

home, for God's sake, take me home!" that finally Pharmaco, who was rolling drunk himself, took pity on him. Getting up from the table, he put the painter's hat on him. "Come on," he said, "I'll take you home." He opened an umbrella, held it over their heads, took the painter by the arm, and began leading him round and round the big table.

The others went on drinking, singing at the top of their lungs, and paying no attention to the two fools who were plodding around the table under an umbrella. Pharmaco led the painter, arm in arm, and circled the table with him once, twice, ten times; in the course of half an hour he led him a total of one hundred times around the table, constantly warning him to hold tight to his hat in this high wind.

The painter walked and walked with Pharmaco, frantically clutching his hat.

"Stick it out, stick it out, you'll be home in a minute!" Pharmaco urged, leading him around the table again. After the hundredth round he stopped with him before the couch that stood by the table, and said to him: "You're home, brother."

"Thank you very much," said the painter, reeling; he undressed, lay down on the couch, and instantly fell asleep. Thereupon the grave-faced Pharmaco, still holding the umbrella over his head, conscientiously circled the table again a hundred times alone, before returning to his seat.

To this day it is a fault of mine that I can love people for that sort of thing.

Later, when I devoted myself exclusively to the theatre, I discovered a similar scene in Shakespeare, in *King Lear*, Act IV, Scene 6, where Edgar leads Gloucester into "the country near Dover." This rather chilled my admiration for Pharmaco. But when still later I learned that Shakespeare had taken the idea from a medieval English play known under the title of The Second Shepherd's Play, where actors symbolize the progress of time and distance by walking in circles around the stage, I acquitted Pharmaco.

Chapter XXIII

THE AIR WAS PERFUMED WITH THE FRESH SCENTS of spring. There were wonderful white lilacs on St. Margaret's Island. The rose gardens there, which chiefly export fine roses to the Balkans, are a particular specialty. Jasmine as well as lilac blossoms there in great luxuriance—two scents that even the most skillful French perfumers can never put successfully into bottles, even though they can make the scent of roses, for example, better than the rose itself can do.

It was eight in the morning when I went strolling over through the sunshine, already warm and kindly, toward a group of lilac bushes, simply for a little walk. All of a sudden I stopped, surprised. I saw the Captain sitting on a bench, with his wife, and in uniform at that. It was nearly five months since I had seen him. He had just been released from prison. I kissed his wife's hand. (I still thought no little of myself in those days for this delicate attention.)

"Here I am," he said. "I will be at your disposal in a moment; I just want to finish this first."

He had a small piece of paper in his hand. From it he was reading aloud oddities he had copied from the books in the prison library in order to show them to his wife when he got out. "You never know what makes you fat," observes a Hungarian proverb. The writer never knows when he is learning. It seems strange when I think now that after such an introduction in such a fashion I learned the following things that morning:

"The Amazon River, emptying into the sea, preserves its strange color far from its mouth, even in the ocean."

"The ocean is not horizontal everywhere, as one would suppose. Ships sailing into the Gulf of Bengal have scientifically determined that the sea rises like a gentle hill toward the Gulf. The cause is unknown. It may be the attraction of high mountains."

"Gaurisankar, the king of the Himalayas and the highest mountain on earth, is still growing, according to accurate measurements; it grows higher from year to year." (An encouraging example for anyone who thinks he has reached the summit of his career.)

"The penguins at the North Pole go about in groups, each group being led by a bird leader. When two groups meet, the leaders greet each other with a movement of the head like a human salutation."

"The expedition led on behalf of the British government by Colonel Younghusband to Lhassa, the capital of Tibet, was fired upon by the Tibetans with cannon whose barrels were leather and whose balls were stone."

All these things were deeply stamped on my memory—and no wonder. I was amazed at the Captain. He seemed calmer than he had been. You could almost have described his eyes as serene.

"I changed in prison," he said, reading the doubt in my eyes as he always did with his unfailing instinct. "I have become another man. Until I was locked up, I was a depressed person, with occasional wild outbursts of temperament. I felt like a man tormented by a crushing burden of debt. In prison I had a surprise. Every day I spent behind the bars I could feel that I was making a small payment on my great debt. And when I came out, I had the wonderful feeling that the whole debt was repaid."

I believed him. His whole bearing indicated it. "And what are your plans now?" I asked.

"You'll be amazed," he said. "I'm thinking of

going into competition with you. I mean to write.
I read a lot of books in prison. I began to feel like
trying my hand."

"What are you going to write?"

"A detective novel. The atmosphere of prison in-
spired me—the whole background, all the sinners,
the convicts—you know."

His wife could feel what he was longing for at
this moment. She said with motherly tenderness,
"You tell him."

He asked with a timid smile, "Shall I tell him?"

"Of course."

His eyes suddenly came alive, with the same gleam
that he had had long ago when he began to tell his
stories.

"Well, you see, there's a rich man, a hypochon-
driac, who goes through life with a nervous fear of
being apparently dead and buried or burned alive.
There are such people. Our man, an elderly gentleman, falls ill. This so increases his fear that he makes
his family solemnly vow to pierce his heart with a
dagger before he is buried if he should die. We've
often heard of that kind of thing, now, haven't we?
The man dies. The family entrusts to the nephew,
who is his chief heir, the fulfillment of his uncle's
last will. The nephew goes to the bier, where the dead
man lies in state among candles, and plunges a long
dagger into his heart. To his utter dismay the wound
begins to bleed—a sign that the old man was still

alive when his heart was pierced; his forebodings had not deceived him. Thus it was actually his nephew, the chief legatee, who murdered him." He was silent, waiting for the effect.

"Well—and?"

"That's only my starting-point. Now the nephew has to behave like a murderer. He has to conceal the blood, tell lies, tremble in fear of discovery, and so on and so forth. Is it good?"

"Good; yes, I think so."

It suddenly occurred to me that he was telling the truth when he said prison had improved him. Before prison, in the days of his glory, he would have told this as a true occurrence. "A friend" would have done it. After the eleventh plum brandy he would have told the story as if he himself had been the murderer.

He looked at me mistrustfully. "Is it good?"

"Good; yes, I think so," I repeated.

His wife said tenderly to me, "It would be sweet of you if you could help him out, being an author, with a little good advice."

"Well, if you don't mind my saying so, it might be well to talk to a doctor before you write the novel."

"Why?"

"To make sure such a case is possible at all from the medical standpoint."

He cried almost angrily, "I shan't talk to any

doctor. He'd be sure to spoil my story. When you write a story yourself, do you get experts to check up on you? A chemist, or an engineer, or a doctor?"

"If my subject demands it I always show it to an expert. I don't want any mistakes in a story."

"You shouldn't do that. A story is fine just as long as you can smell the perfume of the lie about it."

" 'Perfume of the lie'? What do you mean?"

"That's what you professional writers call 'the poetic element.' I'm a romanticist. What is a romanticist? A man who lives his life as if a poet were constantly prescribing what he was to do. And what is a poet? A liar of intellectual stature. I shall write my book as I have already thought it out. I shall write it on shipboard."

"On shipboard?"

"I'm going away, far away. To Africa—hunting."

"Lion-hunting?"

"No. Hunting for ladies' hats. There's a little expedition going to Africa—mostly broken-down young aristocrats—hunting exotic birds. Paris milliners pay large sums for the feathers of these birds. You know what a dead shot I am. We're starting next month. It'll be a hard life, but we shall make a lot of money."

"For heaven's sake," I said to him, "what about the uniform? What does it mean? Are you still wearing it?"

His wife nodded her approval to me. "Yes, don't you think so? I tell him so too, but it's no use. He's like a silly child."

The Captain looked at me—not with his old glance, but wearily, I might almost say softly. "Why not?" he said, vexed.

"But if you'll forgive me," I said, "who ever heard of such a thing? You're going to have all kinds of trouble again."

A very gentle smile played around his mouth. Then, just as children look when the teacher says to them, "You needn't be afraid to look me in the eye," he raised his head and looked into my eyes. His gaze was perfectly innocent and childlike. His lips twitched nervously in a slight grimace. "But suppose I just like to?" he said defiantly.

It was then that I saw for the first time, and also for the last, the little pink rim between his eyeball and eyelid gradually beginning to gleam, and under his romantic violet-blue iris the tiny flush (which a disciplined man can halt just at the last moment before the outburst) sparkling damply.

I never saw him again.

Chapter XXIV

IN THE FALL OF THAT YEAR I WENT ABROAD. I WAS in Geneva, Paris, and London. For a year I was not at home. Returning one October day, I saw the city for the first time as I came from the station after my long absence, and an oppressive feeling stole over me. My generation was quite familiar with the sensation of coming back from Paris or London to the apparently deserted Hungarian capital. The arrival was particularly painful of an evening. An ill-lit station, rather dark streets, the small flow of traffic, so tiny that it was still unregulated and harassing, more dangerous than London's noisiest tumult.

I imagine Budapest owes the metropolitan greatness that it has since acquired to those arrivals. People coming in thus were full of plans and reforms, more than one of which has since been realized. I have never seen such a degree of creative patriotism in the inhabitants of any other town as I have in the people of our city. Wherever I have been with another Hungarian abroad, whenever we saw any excitingly fine new ideas, one of us was sure to exclaim, "They ought to try that at home!" Many are the nocturnal walks in Paris and London that I remember when we worked until dawn upon plans for the beautification of Budapest, for the development of its traffic and its social life.

As aforesaid, I arrived, and the following morning, rested from the travail of the journey by a refreshing night's sleep, I savored to the full the customary first day after a long absence, when everyone is pleasant, everyone handsome, everyone smiles, and warmth comes out to you from every face—the warmth of the great and unfortunately short-lived gratitude that you have not shown yourself for such a long time. The fresh "When did you get here?" that later turns into a weary "How long are you staying?"

Among my plans and reforms the one that occupied me most was one I had already worked out, and even put on paper, in the train—a small but very exclusive club to include all the serious artists, writers, and prominent scholars living in the city. It was to be called the Club of a Hundred, and have just a hundred members. I told my friends about the idea, which won general approval. A friend of mine who has since died, an architect, was particularly enthusiastic, and wanted to organize the charter membership of the club from among the members of our regular table at the café.

The first thing we had to do was to find quarters. One of the other interested parties recommended a splendid clubhouse. In a small side street off the Andrassy ut was a little chateau, which the counts who built it had sold to banking barons. The bankers in turn disposed of it to a so-called "*cercle*" established for the purpose of gambling, and the *cercle* was to pay off the price in installments out of income. It was to, if it could.

But it could not. Our friend's information indicated that the *cercle* was near bankruptcy, and anxious to get rid of the house, while the bankers would let it go on the same terms to some substantial group. So one evening we went with my friend to see what this gambling hell was like. We went all over it, from kitchen to cellar; it was a really comfortable, dainty little chateau, and we were quite on fire as we went through this worst gambling den of the city, imagining the little palace already our own.

The headwaiter of the club was an old acquaintance of ours. This was no accident. It would have been surprising if there had been any headwaiter in Budapest who was not an old acquaintance of mine. He took us through the unaristocratic gathering, whose members did not know each other any too well, for the method of joining the "club" was to buy a membership card at the checkroom for twenty crowns.

When we had inspected the building, the headwaiter led us down to the ground floor, to the checkroom. We had only checked our hats, for it had been a pleasant, warm, fall evening when we got there, and neither of us had brought a coat. When we looked out the front door, a vicious fall rain was pouring down, and the wind was howling. We sent for a carriage. The boy rushed out twice, three times, and each time he came back soaked to the skin but without a carriage. On account of the rain you could not find one anywhere around.

So there we stood, baffled.

"Wait a minute!" the headwaiter suddenly said. "We'll have a coat in a moment. I'll lend one of you mine, and the other gentleman—" He turned to the man behind the hat-check counter. "Give this gentleman the Captain's coat." He mentioned the name as well. It was my Captain—"the Captain of St. Margaret's" as they called him—my romantic teller of tales. After a year and a half I should certainly not have thought of him myself.

"What?" I asked. "Is the Captain here?"

"Did you know him?" said the headwaiter.

"Surely I did," said I. "Why do you say 'did'?"

"He died," he said with a hint of pity.

"When?"

"Last summer. Suicide."

At such moments of bitter surprise one does not usually ask the thing that matters. I snapped at him, "When?"

He managed to fish the date from his memory, approximately.

At that time I was, as I have been since, plagued by the idea of determining exactly what I was doing at the hour and moment of some awful disaster.

For a time I could not read the murders in the papers any more, for if I saw that two masked bandits had crept through the house of an old tobacco woman somewhere in the suburbs and killed her with an ax to rob her—yesterday evening at just eleven—I found no rest until I discovered I had been eating supper at that moment in a little restaurant after the opera, and in fact had been heaping reproaches upon the waiter who had taken my order and had not come back until five minutes later to report apologetically that there was no more chopped goose. At this moment at the edge of town, a poor woman sat up in bed and looked with frozen horror at the ax that would split her skull in a moment. It is an agonizing and instructive and, I think, educational game. (I had to give it up, because it assumed morbid proportions. If I was at a concert, while listening breathless to a passage that the violinist let slowly die away, the thought would flash through my mind: at this moment a ship is going helplessly to the bottom, or somewhere far away on some snow-covered steppe a farmer is looking for his revolver while bandits beat upon his door, and the children hide in the hayloft.)

I discovered that when the poor Captain had picked up the revolver (with which he had shot down so many firemen and schoolboys), I had been sitting in front of the Café Américain in Paris. It was not hard to ascertain this, because I sat there every evening. I sat there looking at the iron basket that stood among the little marble tables, filled with glowing coke to warm the patrons even sitting on the street of a cool night. (How could one go about introducing that at home? I was wondering, while the Captain was putting an end to the life he had loved so much.) That day had been cold in Paris, and apparently warm in Budapest.

It was hard to imagine the Captain dead, lying in state in a coffin. I remembered what he had once said to me about the vanity of the dead. "You have to be tactful to the dead," he said. "Even the dead man has his last little vanity. As the dead man lies there among the candles, he doesn't like people around him whispering, 'Good God, how the poor fellow has changed.' That annoys the dead man. Say, 'He looks as if he were asleep.' That's what he likes to hear."

The hat-check man brought the yellow coat that hung at the end of the long coatrack. "This is the poor Captain's coat," he said, offering it to us.

"Was he a member of the club?" I asked.

"Yes indeed. He came every day."

"Did he play?"

"Every day."

"Was he lucky?"

"Now and then. Mostly he lost. Owed a lot of money. Whatever he won, I think women took away from him again."

"Women?"

"Every evening some lady came to fetch him for supper. Sometimes it was his wife, but mostly it was a little black-haired actress."

He saw the surprise in my face. "A certain Mercedes Pallay," he said in a low voice. "A pretty girl. Pretty and unfortunate."

"Unfortunate?"

"A talented girl; wanted to be an actress, but couldn't."

Headwaiters in Budapest know everything. He leaned over and whispered in my ear, "Quite gifted, but almost completely deaf."

I was silent for eight or ten seconds. Then I pointed to the coat. "A raincoat? Didn't he wear his uniform?"

"In the end he gave it up."

"How does it happen that his coat is still hanging here?"

"It was left here," explained the headwaiter. "It was a pleasant evening when they went home, and he said to the hat-check man who was starting to help him into his coat, 'Never mind, leave it there. It's warm now. Why should I lug it?' That night he blew his brains out. Since then the coat has been hanging here, an orphan. But whenever we get unexpected bad weather and a gentleman has no coat, he wears this one home and brings it back next day. The coat goes out on calls, like a cab."

We did not take the raincoat. They hung it back in place. It hung on its hook like a suicide—the faithful raincoat that had hung itself in grief over its master. It revolved slowly, quietly, on the hook.

"I didn't know your Captain," said my friend the architect, "but I don't like the idea of putting on a dead man's coat. And I hate the people who avidly move into an apartment that has been vacated because someone died there. As a man I'm not interested in widows. They give me the shudders. Let's leave."

Our club came to nothing, but in the course of the negotiations we went to the place once or twice more. Each time I looked at the yellow raincoat before I left. It hung sadly at the end of the coatrack; it was quite alone, separate from the happy coats with a master, with numbered tags worn proudly on their chests like medals.

The last time I went back the coat was not there. "Where's the raincoat?" I asked the hat-check attendant.

"It's bad weather, and then we usually lend it out. Today Mr. Szabo took it, because his girl had called for him in a carriage, and the two of them held it over themselves."

I remembered the story he had once told on the island of the two lovers who had died in the burning house, and the military greatcoat that he covered them over with. How can I ever tell him that his orphan raincoat continued to be true to his spirit in its matter-of-fact, simple way?

Chapter XXV

SOME YEARS LATER, EARLY ONE FRIDAY MORNING, I moved away from St. Margaret's Island forever. I had lunch at noon of the day before with Pharmaco on the little terrace of the hotel (which had long since ceased to be a hydropathic establishment, and was merely a hotel now). That afternoon the heat was terrific, and unusually stuffy for us. It pressed down on your head like a hat. If you took off your straw, you felt as if you had another hat on your head, a warmer, heavier, tighter one.

On the terrace a gentleman who was ordering lemon ice cream said: "In two weeks Serbia will give us everything we ask in our ultimatum."

The heat grew ever more unbearable.

A voice said: "Oh, to be naked, take a bath, and not get dressed again until night!" A gray veil spread over the sun in the sky. Then came another, a dirty, yellowish brown. The air was immobile.

A voice said: "It's like bathing in molten lead." Another dark veil spread over the sun. Pharmaco and I went to my room. Nervously we flung off our clothes—on chairs, tables, on the floor. Outside the window the tremendous trees stood perfectly motionless. Somehow they seemed to feel the coming storm and lightning, far away—sooner than we human beings did.

A friend, a newspaperman, came into the room. He had come out from town to see me. Catching sight of us, he too silently flung off his clothes. "The city is all silly and nervous," he said.

"The heat," said Pharmaco.

"No," said the journalist, "Serbia."

Suddenly it grew dark. It was four o'clock. Faint thunder came from a great distance. There was a slight wind, too, a gentle zephyr. The trees sighed. More thunder.

"Here it comes," said Pharmaco.

"There's a heavy load on my heart, on my lungs," said the newspaperman.

"Low air pressure," said Pharmaco.

"No, Serbia," said the newspaperman, flinging himself on the bed. The bells came from across the Danube. The wind howled, and a darkness like night came down upon us. The rain was already drumming somewhere on a tin roof. There was a terrific crash high up in the heavens. The twelve trees leaned over sideways. From somewhere beyond the building the storm came rushing out, laying them low. There was the tinkle of broken windowpanes. Curtains of water flapped in the air. A woman gave a scream of fright. Thunder, crashing; not a sign of what we had known as rain—nothing but great curtains of water, everywhere. The wail of sirens from the city.

At six o'clock we walked across the battered island. The newspaperman had been urgently summoned to the press department of the Prime Minister. It had stopped raining, but the sun did not appear; the air was stifling.

What did the Prime Minister want of the journalist? Surely it would not be war?

Getting to my office, I learned that the editor-in-chief had been asked to call on the Prime Minister, Count Tisza, for half past ten that night; there was to be important news for the press. The editor-in-chief nervously smoked one cigarette after another. He paced his room in silence. We stood in a corner, like frightened children.

What was all this today? The Last Judgment? Uprooted trees, lightning, thunder, hurricane, tolling bells, sirens, urgent newspaper conferences at night . . .

A fellow-worker whispered in my ear, "We're marching on Serbia." In another corner I caught a scrap: "The Prime Minister has called the city editors in to see him tonight."

We went to a café. All the telephone booths were occupied. Impatient people stood in line outside the booths.

At eleven-thirty a large car stopped outside the

café. Everyone jumped up from the tables. A man came in, whispered something to somebody at a table, and in an instant the place was empty. The big car sped away; twelve people were standing, sitting, or clinging aboard. For the first time I heard the word: *"Haboru."* In Hungarian the word *haboru*, meaning *war*, is a rough, harsh word; it sounds like miniature thunder. Broadside sheets, printed in haste, lay scattered and trampled in the street.

"Six o'clock Saturday evening!" a man shouted.

Standing in the midst of a group, another was reading out the points of the ultimatum.

A voice shouted: "The Serbs will live up to all the points."

Someone said: "I'm going home to sleep." Another yelled after him: "And you can sleep *now?*" "Well, I'm going to try," the man shouted back.

At three in the morning the city grew weary, and fell silent. I went back to the island to pack. I did not know why I was packing or where I was going. I packed feverishly.

Pharmaco helped me. "I'm thirty-five years old. Do you think I'll be called up right away if they mobilize?"

I had a headache. Everyone around me in the hotel was asleep. Was the Prime Minister sleeping? Four in the morning. Had the Kaiser in Vienna waked up yet? He used to get up at five. Perhaps he would get up earlier today.

I sent for a carriage, stowed away my baggage in it, and drove off over the bridge and into town. Pharmaco joined me in the carriage, and went along as far as the bridge. The sky was pale green in the east. The sound of military bugles came across the Danube from the city.

"If the poor Captain had lived to see this," said Pharmaco, "he would have mounted his horse tomorrow and rushed into battle."

"Right. The Captain always imagined that at the beginning of war he would buckle on his saber, leap up into the saddle, and charge into battle at a gallop. Yes, the Captain . . ."

Since childhood I, like the Captain, had lived in the consciousness of being born to the serene calm of a poor but cheerful little country apart from the passions of great nations, in a peaceful, cultivated age that rejoiced in new discoveries. Now, tired, with my head leaning against the back of the carriage seat, I could feel that I was in the very middle of the world, and that the whole unrest of mankind had broken forth at that spot in the globe, where a volcano muttered which we had not even dreamed of.

That morning I left the island forever. The day before had been July 23, 1914, a Thursday. Never before or afterward was there such a terrific storm. It seemed bent on taking away from our city suddenly, but for all time, our gaiety, frivolity, lighthearted romance, even our happiness in being alive. And it did.

Three months later in a little town called Novy-Sandetz, in the north, in Galicia, a young surgeon in an improvised military hospital took my arm one morning and said he wanted to show me something that I could write about in the papers.

Taking me to a room where wounded soldiers were washing, he pointed silently to two Hungarian privates. Both had had amputations. One had lost his left arm, the other his right. They were using their hands, as people do whom God has left in possession of their arms—only they washed cooperatively: one man washed his left hand with the other man's right.

From then on it was not so hard for me to forget the Captain, Pharmaco, the black-haired girl, the champagne mixed with beer and the chiming horses and gypsy music and merriment and romance, all that sinful young life I had lived on St. Margaret's Island.